Little Heroes

HOW WE LIVE
WITH KIDNEY DISEASE

Copyright © 2004

Canadian Cataloguing in Publication Data

Main entry under title:
Little Heroes

Little Heroes
ISBN 0-9734064-0-2

Published by: The Little Heroes Project Team

This book is dedicated to all of the children and their families who are living with kidney disease – past, present and future.

*Even more amazing than the wonders
of nature are the powers of the spirit.*

Helen Keller

Introduction

The *"Little Heroes – How We Live with Kidney Disease"* book is a collection of 25 stories from children and their families at the Winnipeg Children's Hospital. Each of these stories is a personal journey through kidney disease – some are happy and some are sad, but all reveal the depth and strength that is the human spirit.

When I think of the children and families I have been fortunate enough to work with as a kidney nurse, I have truly seen the human spirit in action. I have often been amazed by the strength, determination and will of these children and their families and I am reminded of a story originally written by Erma Bombeck. The story describes how God goes about selecting the parents of children with special life needs. As the story goes, the criteria for each parent seems to be a list of qualities such as the ability to laugh and cherish the positive times, a degree of patience and yet the ability to, at times, be selfish enough to keep their independence all the while helping their child to live in a world where they need to rise above ignorance, cruelty and prejudice. The story ends when God is asked by one of his angels who the patron saint of the family will be and the reply is – they need only look into a mirror. The families who have shared their real life journeys through this book have all of the qualities listed in Erma Bombeck's story and many, many more.

The idea for this book came from the *"Heroes – 100 Stories of Living with Kidney Failure"* publication, with personal stories of adults living with this disease. In 1998, I read the "Heroes" book and thought – what a great resource for families living with kidney disease, but wouldn't it be wonderful if there were something similar for children and their families? And so, the idea for *Little Heroes* was born.

The stories in *Little Heroes* were collected from children and families who volunteered to share their experiences. Some families submitted written stories while a volunteer interviewed others. Although edited, the story content stays true to the original information provided.

I am grateful to Sandra McCallum and the Heroes project team from Royal Victoria Hospital at McGill University Health Centre in Montreal for allowing us to adapt their idea for children and their families. I would especially like to thank Sandra for her continued encouragement and guidance in the early stages of the *Little Heroes* project.

My deepest and most heartfelt thanks go to the families and children who have opened their lives and shared their stories to make *Little Heroes* a reality. Like the project team, they hope this book brings the reader some sense of what it is like to live with kidney disease, as well as some encouragement, and most of all some hope.

Julie Strong
Little Heroes Project Team

Donor Acknowledgements

The printing, publishing and distribution of the Little Heroes book would not have been possible without the financial and in-kind donations from the following companies, groups and organizations:

Bristol-Myers Squibb Pharmaceutical Group
Kidney Foundation of Canada – Manitoba Branch
Jan Smith (illustrations – used with permission: Kidney Foundation of Canada)
Fresenius Medical Care
Janssen-Ortho Biotech Inc.
Serono Canada Inc.
Baxter Corporation
The Chamois Car Wash, Winnipeg, Manitoba
Market Force Inc.
Hignell Book Printing
The Children's Hospital Foundation of Manitoba Inc.

The Little Heroes Project Team salutes and thanks you for your support with this project.

Table of Contents

Stephanie

Angela Nelson is the mother of Stephanie, a 16-year-old girl who received a kidney transplant from her uncle in 2002.

A Mother's Point of View

Let me tell you about my daughter. Her name is Stephanie and she is a caring, giving 16-year-old girl with a terrific sense of humour and an infectious smile. She had all the usual childhood illnesses – chickenpox, colds, sore throats, etc. A year-and-a-half ago her life changed forever.

All the things we take for granted in life – growing up, going to school, having fun with friends and family and, most importantly, our good health – took a bad turn for Stephanie. Suddenly every few days she started to feel like she was going to throw up in the mornings and felt dizzy when she was at school. When she started feeling like this every day I knew this wasn't any ordinary sickness you would think of, like the flu or an upset stomach. Her doctor was very busy at the time and I wasn't able to get an appointment for Stephanie to see her as soon as I wanted. I guess something deep in my mind told me I should get this checked out as soon as possible. I took her to the Misericordia Urgent Care Centre on May 18, 2001. While there, the doctors learned by doing various tests that Stephanie's blood pressure was way too high and went on to do some blood and urine

> I wanted so badly to wave a magic wand and have it all go away, but I couldn't.

testing. The results of these tests showed that she was suffering from end-stage kidney failure. More specialized tests showed that one of her kidneys was very tiny when she was born and never worked to help rid her body of waste products. The other one didn't grow as large as it should have and slowly started to shut down as she grew older. In other words, she couldn't 'pee' out all the liquids she drank and they were very slowly poisoning her blood.

The first feeling I remember having when I heard this news was one of disbelief. Why her? How could such a tragic thing happen to an innocent child? We cried together that day in the hospital for a long time. I felt so angry and helpless at the same time. I wanted so badly to wave a magic wand and have it all go away, but I couldn't. Although it seems impossible, I managed to set these feelings aside and concentrate on what could be done for Stephanie to make her feel better. I also realized I had to remain strong emotionally for her because naturally she felt upset, sad and very scared about what was going to happen next.

'Dialysis' was a word I always read about or saw on television. A former schoolmate of mine was on dialysis for many years but I never really understood what it meant. I sure learned in a hurry. Most of you who are reading this book have probably already had it explained to you.

Either method of dialysis had its ups and downs. Stephanie tried home dialysis first. She was hooked up to her machine from 8 to 10 hours every night. We had problems with this: the one most annoying for Stephanie was that she had to be in bed very early on school nights and was stuck in her room for such long periods of time. Also, cleaning the machine and the bags and hooking everything up every night was sometimes just too much for both of us. Then she'd have problems during the night – usually a kinked tube – which would lead to a bad night's sleep and a hard time for her functioning at school and me to work the next day. On the positive side, the machine was small enough (although very heavy!) that Stephanie was able to take a trip to Toronto with her school band. I was very nervous at that time because she hadn't been away from home since her illness began (except for hospital stays). I was proud to know once she returned that she had used the machine successfully and had taken her numerous medications and had a pretty good time, all things considered.

Hemodialysis was never easy. Having to have two tubes injected into your arm every other day is no easy task. Stephanie was always anxious and afraid on those many trips to the hospital, but a very brave girl at the same time. She would usually feel much better after a session, but if she didn't stick to her 4-cup per day fluid restriction the whole procedure could make her feel quite ill.

As I mentioned, Stephanie had many, many pills to take to help her feel better. This, too, wasn't easy at first because she had a really, really hard time swallowing pills. Luckily, over time she got used to it and does much better now.

Stephanie always tried to make the best of her situation but it was always tough to arrange her school and social life around the dialysis and numerous clinic visits. I will always admire her strength and ability to carry on in spite of this. I believe children are an amazing group of people who possess more stamina and courage than we give them credit for.

During all this turmoil the search was on for a donor to give Stephanie a new kidney. I prayed and prayed every night for this precious moment. I even told Santa Claus this was all I wanted for Christmas! Miracles never cease and after many, many tests, we were told that Stephanie's uncle, my brother, Bill, was a match. The surgery took place on May 23, 2002. What a day that was – waiting and waiting for that moment to hear that the operation was a success and donor and recipient were doing fine. It was late afternoon when I finally heard the good news and again I cried and cried, this time tears of pure joy.

After about a week in the hospital Stephanie came home looking better than she ever had. She bounced back wonderfully and to this day continues to do very well. There are still many trips to the hospital for blood tests and check-ups, but as long as the news is all good, I don't mind at all. Now she has to drink more than she did even before she got sick. To anyone who thinks drinking 8 to 12 cups of liquid a day is easy, just try it – we don't drink as much as we think we do. Stephanie will have to take very good care of her new kidney each and every day by faithfully taking her medications and fluids, but will live a reasonably normal, active life now.

For anyone out there considering going to be tested as a donor, I offer the following from my dear brother, Bill, to who we owe the return of Stephanie's spirit: "When you have a chance and are given a choice while alive to save a life, why not give an organ if you are compatible and able. Giving another person the opportunity to enjoy the beauties of this great land is a gift from the heart."

My advice to all children and their parent(s)/caregivers going through an ordeal like this is: Listen to the doctors and nurses and ask questions about anything you don't understand. Family and friends will offer support – take it. Try hard through all the bad times to remember that life is a fragile gift and no matter how we must live it we must do so with courage. Cry if you need to, but don't forget to laugh. Be as brave as you can for each other, support each other and most of all, remember, love endures all.

Stephanie

As we read the courageous battles of the children in this book, someone's child may be receiving the news that they have kidney disease. It will change your life but don't let it change who you are inside.

Our prayers are with all of you.

Laura

Laura Friesen is a 17-year-old girl diagnosed with Hemolytic Uremic Syndrome at the age of five. Her treatments have included peritoneal dialysis, hemodialysis and a transplant.

There is nothing that I can't do.

I would like to be very clear about something from the beginning. I am not a hero in any way, shape or form. The term I like to use is *person.* On some days, it seems like kidney disease is a very small part of my life, and some days it's right there staring me in the face. I try not to undervalue my life changing experience with the disease, but there isn't really any excuse for me to live beneath my potential at this point.

I have had my transplanted kidney for nine years. I probably don't appreciate it as much as I should. When I was five I learned I had Hemolytic Uremic Syndrome. I was on hemodialysis for about a year and lived in and out of the hospital for the same amount of time. My mom donated one of her kidneys to me in 1992. My recovery was fairly smooth with one bad rejection episode when I was ten or eleven. They pumped me full of prednisone through an I.V. and I had to miss camp that summer because I was sick. The time I spent in the hospital was time I should have been spending outside with my friends. One thing I remember from the hospital is my sixth birthday party held in the ward's lounge. I also remember being on CHTV (Children's Hospital Television Station) with No-Name, the

♡*Laura*

station's puppet. I remember eating lightly toasted tuna salad sandwiches on white bread (I had one every day) after my transplant. In the OR I remember falling asleep with my toy bunny right by my head. The nurses on my ward were always really good. So I definitely have positive memories of my time in the hospital, and I've forgotten the negative ones.

There is nothing that I can't do. If I want to do something I do it. I love music and drama, take private music lessons and play the saxophone in two bands at school. I always participate in the productions my school puts on and I would love to pursue acting further one day. I've always been an honor roll student and occasionally had the opportunity to do something special because of that. My friends and I often do things together on Friday nights like watch movies. I have a job at a small restaurant in my town. This summer I'm going to jazz camp with my best friend.

I would never consider not taking my medications because they are helping me to do all the things I want to do. Maybe to some people it would seem a hassle and a sign that they're unhealthy – "I shouldn't have to take pills to be normal like everyone else." The medications are what make me able to do normal things like everyone else. I try not to use my disease as an excuse to not measure up to my potential. I would like to be successful and do something important, but I would also be content with being happy and healthy and doing something that I love.

There are a lot of "nuisances" to having this disease. It can be a struggle to remember to take my medication with my busy life. My clinic appointments cause me to miss school and fall behind in my studies. I often don't feel well due to the side effects and complications of the drugs. I also have the usual social, family, and school difficulties. I often don't deal with them very well. But I am committed to making my life better and more full. My activities help me enjoy and live my life to the fullest. I'm happy doing the things that I do. That's the main goal – to be happy and healthy with your life as a kidney patient.

Sometimes I worry about when my kidney will fail and if I'll need another transplant. Who would donate their kidney to me? Will I have to be on dialysis for a lengthy amount of time? Will something come in the way of my career or my goals? Will my health problems shorten my lifespan considerably? There's no way of knowing these things right now. I guess I'm really just living day-by-day, appointment-to-appointment.

So, if that was my story, there it is. I hope it can and will encourage someone out there. Another encouraging thing that is really good is Ben and Jerry's Bovinity Divinity ice cream. Also, nothing makes me feel better that buying a new pair of shoes that I love!

Laura 💙

When Laura (age six) was in the hospital, she liked to write stories about her toy bunny. One of these stories she wrote for her cousins who lived far away in Africa. Her aunt wrote back with the following letter.

December 10, 1993
Dear Laura,

I would like to tell you a story that I thought of last night. I haven't thought of a bunny story, but I thought of a kidney story.

Well, this kidney was just an ordinary kidney, and kidneys are not the smartest organs in the body. (Actually the brain is the smartest organ), and sometimes the kidney did not feel too important. He didn't know that he was doing an important job that no one else could do. God had a special plan for this kidney even though no one knew about it yet.

One day Kidney heard there was going to be an operation, but he didn't worry about it. Suddenly, he found out he was part of the operation and he was being lifted out of his warm place. Oh no! What was happening to him? Where was he going? Suddenly, he found himself in another warm body and he was being fitted and attached to this new body. "Hmm! This body seems smaller and cozier. I think I'm going to like it here. I know I'm not the smartest organ, but I can do one job very well. God gave me one job, and that is cleaning the blood and making urine."

"Well, here comes some blood! Let's get to work! Let's show this new body that we can work." Soon the kidney had cleaned a lot of blood and made a bunch of urine. The new body felt so much better. The little girl had been sick for one year and now she was finally starting to feel better.

Kidney passed the urine on to the bladder. Now it was Bladder's turn to be surprised. He had not done any work since the old kidneys got sick. Well he knew what to do. He collected the urine until he was full, then he sent a message to the little girl, Laura. "It's time to go to the bathroom. I hope you haven't forgotten how because I'm feeling full."

Kidney was very thankful now that he was a kidney and not a brain or a heart. God had given him an important job to do, and only he could save Laura's life. He liked his new home and he liked Laura. He knew now, that when she jumped rope, ran, and rode her bike, it was because he was doing his job to keep her healthy.

The End

That's my little story. I hope you liked it. I read it to your cousins and they liked it. You are a special girl and I love you very much.

Love, Auntie Beverly

♡Laura

Shirley

*Shirley is a 13-year-old girl who was on
hemodialysis at the time she wrote this poem.
She received a cadaveric transplant in July 2001.*

*I am a little girl in a
Renal failure world.*

*I have to go to hemo and I
Have to eat just right,
Or my potassium and calcium
Will climb up out of sight.*

*My blood pressure's a
Problem and I have to keep it good,
By giving up my favorites
—All the salty food.*

*I know if I keep healthy and
Try hard every day,
I'll be ready for a transplant
When it comes my way.*

Shirley and Mama J

William

Janie and Walter Epp are the parents of seven year-old William, who was born with ARPKD and whose treatments have included peritoneal dialysis and a transplant.

"I will lie down in peace and sleep, For you alone, O Lord, will keep me safe." Psalm 4:8

In July 1994, my husband, Walter, and I were expecting our third child. During a routine ultra-sound examination our doctor discovered something unusual. Rather than guess at a diagnosis, he sent us to Health Sciences Centre, Women's Hospital. Walt and I met with the neonatal expert in Winnipeg the very next day, and the news wasn't very hopeful.

He told us in no uncertain terms that this baby would not live after birth. He had determined that the baby had a disease known as Autosomal Recessive Polycystic Kidney Disease. This condition had prevented the formal development of kidney tissue. In fact, the kidneys were enlarged and had prevented the proper development of his lungs. I remember very distinctly his words to us. "When this child is born it will not live. When it is born it will die, because there are no lungs for it to draw breath."

We were in shock; not doubting for an instant what the doctor had told us was fact, but disbelief that this could happen to us. Our child had only six weeks to live, and then he would die on the day he was born.

We were sent home, a three and a half hour trip spent in silence. All of my thoughts were focused on the baby. This was not what we had planned for. We had planned to have three children, and not in our worst nightmares considered that we would have to bury the third one. Grief overtook us and left us weak. Here I was, in the last trimester of my pregnancy, with so much hope in the future our family would be complete!

Walter and I shared this with our families, telling Nicholas, five, and Kaitlin, two and a half, that the baby was sick. They could understand that much, and they could also see the grief in the faces around them. We also shared the news with our church family, and their loving support was what kept us going. With their continued prayer support we relied on God to hold us up.

Walter held to the belief that God could heal our child, and that we just needed to believe. I wanted to believe too, but the child in my stomach, and thoughts of death held me back. I accepted as fact what was to happen. So, we began the vigil of waiting for the date chosen for the delivery. To me, nothing and everything had changed. I was still pregnant and my baby still moved, kicked, slept and occupied my thoughts, along with the fear of what was to come. I could not stop loving this child, and so we waited.

In Brandon hospital that day, every one was prepared to let us have whatever we needed. Our child would be delivered by cesarean section because he was in a sitting position, and was unable to turn due to a lack of amniotic fluid. We had asked the doctor to deliver the baby and give him to us immediately. We knew we would have very little time to hold our child as he died in our arms. I was awake with my husband by my side, as well as a pediatrician and all the other required delivery staff. We also had a friend with us. Someone who was a staff nurse at the hospital; she was a great moral support for us.

The baby was delivered, and Walter held him, laying him across my chest. As we cried, our baby cried. Our son cried, a healthy wail of indignation, and time stood still for us. We were unaware of anyone, or anything other than the three of us.

I don't know if we realized what was happening, but I know we were no longer waiting for death to claim this child of ours! After 20 minutes of everyone standing there wondering what to do, the pediatrician said, "Is it okay if I suction him?" We just laughed and handed him over. After 45 minutes they decided he was not going to die right away, so they prepared me for transfer to a room. At this time, Walter took the baby upstairs to meet his grandparents and our pastor. They all thought he was bringing a dead baby for them to see, they were all in tears. What a shock for them to see this child alive and crying. Our pastor told us later that even at this point he thought they were still waiting for the baby to die!

We had received a miracle! Our baby's lungs had developed in the six weeks that followed that fateful day of the ultrasound. We didn't realize what had happened, we were in such shock. It was later after we had time to think about it, that we realized our miracle.

The doctor had made arrangements for the baby to be transferred to Winnipeg Children's Hospital for examination, since he lived. So, when he was less than 24 hours old he was taken in an incubator to Winnipeg by Life Flight.

Our other children got to meet him and say goodbye. It was very painful for us to let him go, but it was for the best. The doctors in Winnipeg had a chance to see him, and the next day Walter and I went to the Neonatal ICU.

The first time we met one of the doctors there, he gave us all the medical details, and also gave us some of the best advice we have ever been given. He told us that he knew of many families that had faced similar situations, and it was hard on relationships, even leading to divorce. He wanted us to be forewarned. That statement has stuck with us through it all, and brought us up short whenever we've struggled.

During the time that he was in the hospital, and we were at home, I was hit by a sense of unreality. I would phone and ask his nurse what he was doing and how he was, and they had so little to say-so little for a distraught mother on the phone. I felt ambivalence towards all of them. They were there with him and I couldn't be. It was a difficult time for me. One bright spot was our trip to see him on the weekends, when I discovered that a woman from the pastoral care program had been in to see William. She wrote a very nice note about what William was doing at the time she visited him. She had left several of these lovely notes, but always during the week when we weren't there. Her little notes were precious to us.

We brought William home after a month in hospital. He was on numerous medications and nasogastric tube feedings around the clock. This took its toll on us, as Walter was still harvesting our crops, and I was home with the three kids. Homecare was involved in the beginning, they could come and do care for William for a few hours, but they could not take care of the other two children. I was supposed to do that. With the routine of around the clock care for William I was so exhausted I usually slept on the couch, while the children sat at my feet and watched their "morning shows." Thank God for Mr. Dress Up! It was the start of four and a half years of sleep deprivation.

William

We had decided early on, that if he needed to be in the hospital, that one of us had to go with him. Since I couldn't very easily do the farm chores myself, and Walt was quite capable of doing that and taking care of the children, we decided that I would go. So many times I would be packing a bag and Nicholas and Kaitlen would cry. It was a very difficult time for us. When William was in hospital for longer periods I would quite often drive home during the week, when I was sure there was Child Life staff on duty. I'd be back for the weekend when staffing was lower. I really did feel compelled to be there. My concern for him was sometimes overwhelming. I knew that I could just leave him, and that the staff would care for him, but the thought that we could still lose him was always at the back of my mind. Walter and I did not want him to grow up in the hospital, unaware of family love, and so I kept him in touch with his family through stories I would tell and pictures I would show to him.

I am so thankful for the staff at the hospital. They never judged me or my emotions, but supported me and made sure that I had someone to talk to. It was during this time that I came to understand life on the hospital ward and I gained a new appreciation for the nursing staff. They are very dedicated to the children that they care for. I lost the feelings of ambivalence that I felt earlier, and gained respect for them and what they accomplish in a day.

When William was six months old he lost what little kidney function he had at birth, and had a peritoneal catheter placed in his abdomen. Dialysis was a wonderful change for his health. We watched him blossom...and we watched him suffer through countless infections that were very painful for him. From the beginning, William was on twelve hours of dialysis every day. This was done at home in his bedroom. I was trained to do the therapy and later there were two homecare nurses trained to provide us some respite. They were a real blessing to us because of the twelve hour therapy. We had to be home by seven to start. It gave us some time to be alone with Kaitlen and Nicholas as well.

Dialysis can be a wonderful thing for someone in renal failure, but it was stressful for the rest of us. For the first year, Walter and I took turns each night getting up to straighten kinked tubing, or roll William over on his back. The machine would alarm, and wake us at least ten to twenty times a night. I was the only one of us trained to do the dialysis, and this was sometimes very distressful to me. I would feel angry about how alone I was with it, even though I understood why Walter did not feel able to do the treatments.

Every time William had an infection I had to take him to Winnipeg to the hospital. Usually the trips were late at night and hurried. I actually had a bag packed in the closet for these emergency trips. Over the four and a half years that William was on dialysis he spent 400 days in the hospital. For most of these days I was with him, but there were some times when Walt would drive us there and we would leave him for Respite care in the hospital. They would care for him and I would get the sleep I so desperately needed.

I remember once having a stomach flu, diarrhea and vomiting, and still having to do the therapy because I was told that Homecare was not for emergencies. This was a real heartache for me. What should have been available was not when it was most often needed. As a result I was exhausted for most of those four and a half years. I also suffered through a serious depression during those four years. Exhaustion, the complete change in our lifestyle, and the isolation I often experienced all piled up on me. I wish I could say that I did it all on my own, but I can't. I just thank God for the people he sent into my life that helped me to survive the depression.

Our local Lions Club were big supporters during those years. They did numerous fundraisers on our behalf, and there efforts were very much appreciated. We could hardly afford the ambulance costs, numerous trips to Winnipeg, and our stays at the Ronald McDonald House. We will always have a place in our hearts for the special people in that club and for all the people of Boissevain, who opened their hearts to us and showed what a caring community they are.

Walt and I have been so grateful to the Ronald McDonald House, and the kind staff. Our experiences there have been the best! Meeting people in similar situations gave us insight. We were not the only people in the world whose lives were in turmoil. It is definitely a family place. Sometimes the promise of staying at the house was the only thing that helped Kaitlen and Nicholas get through the many trips to Winnipeg.

We knew that transplant was a someday subject. We would have loved to push the doctors to do it, but we had decided to trust their judgment and we were right to do so. They told us that the window of opportunity would open and then it would be time for the transplant. So we waited. William was on growth hormone, EPO, Calcitriol, and numerous blood pressure medications, and with monthly trips to Winnipeg, we managed to care for him, and love him. He was a part of our family, a vital member.

William was very sick around the age of two. His blood pressure was out of control, and after many drug changes and tests, the doctors decided it was the failed kidneys that caused the high pressure. So, both his kidneys were removed. The change this brought about for William was incredible. He went from seven words to a complete vocabulary and his blood pressure was maintained at a safer level. It was another stage in his life. Language opened up his personality so much. He could make us all laugh!

In 1998, William's doctors started talking about transplant. We were ecstatic! We were scared as well, but anxious to get on with it. Walter and I were concerned about who would be a donor, as I had already donated a kidney to my sister in 1984. We found out that Walter was not a match, and so were faced with finding a donor in our family. We approached both sides of the family, told them that it was time for transplant, and that we needed volunteers. We gave them the phone number for the transplant clinic in Winnipeg and left it to them if they wished to be tested to see if they matched. We prayed that someone would come forward and that it would be a match. It was really a peaceful wait. We knew the time would come, and we were very excited and not too concerned about where the kidney would come from. I really feel that God was giving us peace in the situation just as He has in many other situations that we had faced with William.

Walter's brother, Edward, was a match and he decided to be a donor! He wanted William to have a chance at a better life. William went through the testing required for transplant and we made arrangements for our stay in Winnipeg. We needed to make arrangements to live in the city for three months. Since the children were in school, and we had our cattle to care for, we decided that Walt would stay home and I would stay in Winnipeg with William.

On November 19, 1998, William received the kidney donated by his Uncle Ed. Our families were with us, as well as our pastor. We prayed over both William and Ed, and asked God to go with them to surgery. It was truly a joyous time for us, with some trepidation on Ed's part. He was facing surgery even though he was completely healthy.

> He lives with many limits in his life but refuses to let them beat him.

Surgery went well for both of them. William was in recovery when he asked the nurse to pray for him. I think he may have been scared waking up in a strange room, with I.V.s and machines beeping, and pain in his tummy. William was also saying, "I want life." They thought that was such a profound thing to say, except he really did want LIFE cereal, his favorite food at the time!

William and I were settled into our house in Winnipeg, and into the routine of transplant clinic every morning. We learned all about the medications and the slow recovery that was ahead of him. I really think that the isolation that he felt from being so far from the rest of his family was very hard on him, and he was sad about that. We celebrated Christmas with everyone coming to be with us in Winnipeg. It was strange for all of us, but we were glad to be there together.

On December 31, we packed up and moved home. It was such a relief to go home, even though I knew we still faced weekly trips to the transplant clinic for a while. Those trips really were two day trips for us every week, and so we were tired for the rest of the week!

It has now been just over two years since transplant, and things are going very well. There have been adjustments to medications and routines. William needed to learn to eat like any other child, and this was sometimes a serious problem, especially when he wouldn't eat for days, and needed to be given nasogastric tube feeds. It was a real battle to teach him about the tastes of things, when for so long food held very little appeal to him. He still has cravings for foods, but is also trying a larger variety at mealtime.

William is a very active little boy who loves to play with his sister and brother, and this summer he actually was able to join them, actually running after them. They spent most afternoons in the local pool, and William actually took two levels of swimming lessons, passing with flying colors! He can't touch the bottom of the pool yet, but with a little assistance, can swim across the pool. What a sight that is!

William is currently in first grade and doing well. He loves his teacher and all of the kids in his class. Every day he faces prejudices that he handles very well. He is short for his age, less agile than the others, and has food allergies along with his transplant concerns, that make it easy for him to be isolated. He is a very extroverted, friendly little boy who is unafraid to try. He lives with many limits in his life but refuses to let them beat him. We are very diligent to watch for those instances when he is treated in an infantile way. People always assume that making everything easy for him is the best thing when it is the last thing he needs. Compassion is called for, certainly, but he needs to experience life and learn to work through any problems he runs into. He needs to find the strength in himself, and his ability to think about answers rather than look for people to do things for him. William has spent a great deal of his life disabled by renal failure, but that time is behind him. He needs to be allowed to be an enabled person, and that is what we will continue to teach him and those who come into contact with him.

We would never say we know what the future holds for us, but with God's grace, we will see many more years of good health for William.

Megan

Anita Prince is the mother of Megan Bunn, a 12-year-old girl whose treatments have included peritoneal and hemodialysis. Megan received a cadaveric transplant in August 2003.

Megan has kept on living her life to the fullest; she has not let this disease bring her down.

When my daughter, Megan, was admitted into the Children Hospital May 20, 2000, I never imagined what a change was about to happen. Who would ever think their child would develop a very serious disease? What parents ever think of this? Not very many. I for one didn't.

When I look at my twelve year old daughter today, I thank Creator for her life and her health. When I look at how much kidney disease has changed our lives I would never have thought I would be feeling this way.

When Megan was first diagnosed with Kidney Disease my first thought was "what do these doctors know anyway". It took me until just recently to actually believe and accept that my daughter's life has changed. I was very angry at everyone, the doctors, the nurses, my partner, my mother, Creator, everyone. I could not believe that this was happening to her. I did not want to believe. I was in constant denial. I kept saying that her kidneys would come back, the doctors had made a mistake, I even went so far as to start thinking the doctors just wanted to experiment with my daughter. I didn't want to believe she was sick. It wasn't until after numerous visits and stays in the hospital that my daughter said she wanted to have these protein injections to help combat the ANCA in her blood. ANCA that somehow made their way into my daughter's bloodstream and gotten her sick.

It wasn't until April 2001, one month short of a year that she got sick, that my daughter told me that she wanted to get off her kidney machine and if this was going to help her get off the machine faster then she would go through this procedure. It wasn't until then that I realized I was the one holding back her recovery. My daughter, Megan, had accepted her condition. My daughter had told me the day she had to have an emergency kidney biopsy (almost a year ago) that she wasn't scared, but it was I who had gotten her scared. I started crying when the nurses wheeled her into the operating room. It was my fear that frightened her.

Today when I look back at the changes in our lives I can see how my daughter and I have gotten close. I know that her disease had something to do with it. I think many times of how I have taken my daughter's existence and her health for granted, but with this drastic change I have to thank Creator for everything. I watch my daughter today, and I actually see and hear her. She has given me so much insight and strength. I never imagined a child of 12 could have so much insight, strength and courage. She has taught me so much. I am very grateful for her. Megan has kept on living her life to the fullest, she has not let this disease bring her down.

Watching her you would not know she was on dialysis. I have learned to support her and follow her lead, this is her life, not mine. Megan is the one who has to live with kidney disease and I am only here to help make her life more bearable and comfortable. I have learned to separate my fears from my daughter's.

Today Megan is looking forward to having her transplant and I am supporting her to the best of my ability.

When this disease first hit and changed our lives, in my anger, grief and blame, I could not see my daughter for who she is; a beautiful butterfly, full of life, strength, courage, hope determination and beauty. She is truly a gift. A gift I'll treasure for the rest of my life.

So today I'd have to say good things have come out of this disease, although I would not wish it on any child, or person for that matter, but it happens, and it happened to Megan. I am grateful today that I am able to see this. I thank the Creator for two special people who have helped me work through my fears, anger, grief and blame. I needed some help, I couldn't have done this by myself. I thank the Creator for putting them in my path and helping me heal in order to help and support my daughter in a good and healthy way.

Megwetch,
Zoongizi Ode Ikwe
Anita Prince

Michael

Rob and Lynne Grigat are the parents of Michael, an 8-year-old boy whose treatments have included dialysis and a transplant.

The Boy with the Big Kidney

On February 8th, 1999, our son, Michael, was diagnosed with chronic end-stage renal failure and our world was shattered. We felt that something was not right with Michael a few months prior to this. We started to notice that he was not eating very well. He was very fatigued to the point where his teacher told us he was falling asleep in class, and was not able to do his schoolwork. It was a daily struggle to get him to eat anything, and when he did, it seemed more times than not, he was sick. We were also quite concerned about his rate of growth. Strangers would ask how old he was and be shocked when we replied that he was seven. They thought he was four!

Through our concerns, Michael's pediatrician sent us for blood-work where we learned he was anemic. To our surprise, we were then sent for further testing with a pediatric nephrology team. An ultrasound would prove that Michael's kidneys were shriveled up and not removing waste products from his body.

The initial shock and devastation came when his doctor told us that he would not improve, and that a transplant would be necessary. Aside from being scared to death of what our child would have to face, we all had to be brave to help Michael get the help that was inevitable. Medication began immediately, and regular weekly visits, along with several other tests started to show a slight improvement in Michael. Dialysis was soon going to be necessary and a peritoneal catheter would have to be inserted into his peritoneal cavity, which would need time to heal.

Michael had his first surgery on May 31st, 1999, which went well. In July, Michael was supposed to start dialysis. My husband and I were both trained to perform this at home, along with regular dressing changes (cleaning external catheter and exit site). During our training we had several attempts to try dialysis on Michael, but we ran into a snag. The catheter was not working and a second surgery was needed to try to flip the catheter into the correct position. Still, we tried over and over throughout the next few days to get his catheter working, but again, his doctors felt that they needed to see where the catheter was located.

This time, using laparoscopy to identify the precise whereabouts of the catheter, the doctors told us that it wouldn't work, and would have to be removed. A second catheter was placed on his left side.

Once the second catheter was inserted, his doctors immediately tried dialysis. We thought this would be a sure thing. You begin to think, what are the odds of this not working again? It turned out to be one more setback. Michael now needed surgery for a hernia, which was scheduled for the end of August. We spent almost two weeks in the hospital, and Michael missed the bus to Kidney Camp. He was still able to go with one of his nurse clinicians for half of the week.

> Dialysis became part of our daily routine, which meant that he could still attend school regularly, and be a normal kid.

One week after camp Michael had his surgery and was on his way to dialysis for ten hours, six nights a week. Dialysis became part of our daily routine, which meant that he could still attend school regularly, and be a normal kid.

Michael was incredible at having dressings changed, injections twice a week, taking medications, and being hooked up to his machine. We were thrilled because this meant that he must have been feeling better. We were starting to see the little boy that we hadn't seen in what seemed like a long time. His spirits had picked up and he had more energy. What a great sight!

Michael has continued to see his doctors over the last year. He has been improving each day with the dialysis and regular medications, which have often had to be altered. In May 2000, Michael began to take growth hormone to enhance his growth.

This summer he was able to go swimming at his grandparents' cabin with the use of colostomy bags to cover his exit site and keep his tubing clean from infection. You couldn't have seen a happier kid!

Michael

On August 13th, 2000, Michael was getting packed and ready for another year at Kidney Camp. The next morning he had to be at the departure site at 7 am, unfortunately he never made it, again! The call we thought we wouldn't get for years came at 5:20 a.m. from a doctor that we had never met until that very morning. He told us that Michael wouldn't be going to camp because they had found a possible match. We didn't know whether to jump for joy or cry, so we just sat there letting it sink in. We were told to bring Michael into the hospital as soon as he was finished on his dialysis therapy.

Reaching the hospital at 6:30 a.m., Michael was immediately sent for blood work for a final cross-match. This was a more sensitive test than the ones that had been done routinely each month through his clinic visits. More blood work was needed and an IV was started. Michael was being prepared for surgery even though we hadn't heard the final results yet. We spent the day at the hospital waiting anxiously for the news

It is truly unbelievable the thoughts that passed through our heads. We wondered if we would be sent home if the results were not good. We were informed that we would know by five o'clock that night. As if by some strange coincedence, the same doctor who had called us in the morning called us again at 5:20 p.m. to say that we were good to go! What an amazing moment!

Almost immediately he was taken down to surgery at 6:30 p.m. and it took about three and a half hours. Michael was taken to the PICU shortly after.

To see your own child lying there with several machines hooked up to him is the most terrifying thing I think a parent can face, but we really wanted to concentrate on him getting better. We couldn't understand what he was feeling, but we began to understand that just being there with him was what he needed.

Michael remained in the PICU for five days and was then stable enough to be sent back to the ward. For the next ten days he was closely monitored by his doctors. With each day that passed it began to look as though this kidney was really working. The concern that seemed to rest heavy on our shoulders, since his surgery, still remained. This was something that we all really wanted, but the questions started filling our heads. The doctors were pretty positive and kept reassuring us that he'd be fine, that the kidney just needed some time to get going. This was a large kidney for a small boy. My husband and I went through the motions, but I don't think the reality had really set in.

We had noticed that Michael seemed a little upset and angry after his surgery, as he has after previous surgeries. It upset both my husband, and myself because it seemed to be directed more to the people that were the closest to him. Some days he would be okay and then others he would intolerable.

Finally, Michael was ready to be released, and we weren't sure that it was what we wanted. We felt as though we might not be able to take care of him the way the nurses and doctors had, but we had to do our part and stay strong. It is amazing what you can do when someone depends on you.

Michael is now resting comfortably at home, continuing to see the doctors daily for blood work and transplant clinic. He will need to remain at home to recuperate for two or three months, working with a tutor, but overall he has adjusted well.

In closing I would like to say that Michael is the bravest person that I know. He has been very responsible about taking his medications, something he'll have to endure for the rest of his life. He has remained positive and strong-willed.

This is by far the most precious gift anyone has or ever will give Michael, and I am so thankful to the family that gave our son a second chance at living a normal life. The impact all of this has had on our family has been incredible. It has been a very emotional and stressful year and a half for our family; however, we have been fortunate enough to be surrounded by a wonderful nephrology team. They were there for us ever step of the way. Something that we thought would change our lives forever has really only lasted a short time. It seems like only a few months ago we heard the devastating news, but we have learned a great deal of very useful information that we hope can help others in the near future.

The Grigat Family

Michael

Priscilla

Priscilla Dueck is a 9-year-old girl who received a kidney transplant in March 2001. Priscilla's mom, Doris, donated a kidney to her daughter.

Doris Dueck donated a kidney to her daughter, Priscilla.

I got my kidney from my mom. Before my operation I was always thirsty, but now my thirst is gone. Before my operation I was never really hungry, but now I'm so hungry I can eat a hamburger from McDonalds for breakfast.

The day before my operation they thought the IV was stuck, so when they went to get another nurse we prayed. When the other nurse came she saw that only a little thing had stopped the IV, so she moved it, and then they didn't need to put in a fresh IV. Praise God.

Priscilla was born February 24th, 1992 in Fort Frances, Ontario. We knew that she wouldn't have normal kidneys before she was born. When she was three days old, they flew her to Winnipeg where she was in the hospital for two weeks. My husband, Richard, and I had planned to live in Mexico where Richard's family lives, but since Priscilla had kidney disease we decided to move to Manitoba.

On April 5th to the 20th of 1993, Priscilla was in the hospital in Winnipeg because she was dehydrated. The first two years of her life were very, very hard, thinking of how we had to feed her. Every three hours she had to have milk and it took her so very long to drink it. Lots of the time went into giving her food. After two years it was a bit better, but so many times we had to encourage her to eat. If Priscilla didn't have to eat to live, it sure would have been easier. Priscilla's creatinine was about 400 when she was born, and then it went down as far as 185. It's been going up and down for the last nine years, but as a whole its gone up. It's now 421.

On March 20th, 2001 was the day that Priscilla had her kidney transplant. I gave her the kidney. In all those nine years God didn't let us down once. He was always there to help us. He answered many prayers. God is great and God is good. Priscilla is doing very well with her new kidney. Her breath doesn't smell so bad now, and she eats lots more.

Kidney Camp is the Best

( )

We love kidney Camp

By..Gerlyn

Gerlyn

On our way to Kidney Camp

Carissa

Megan

Robert

Michael

Camp Volunteer Dan (left) with campers Jerry and Robert

Kyle

"Good Days & Bad Days"
by Amber

Amber

good   Bad

Sean

Sean tackles the high ropes (below)

"Before & After" by Shirley

Before I go to Dialysis! I look like this. (Puffy) →

After Dialysis I look like this A little angel. →

Shirley
AGE 10 years 2000

Shirley

Jasmine (right) and buddies on the way to hemodialysis from camp

William 🎈

No Name,
the puppet (from
CHJU-Winnipeg
Children's Hospital)

No Name
William

Robert 🎈

Camp Volunteers

Dr. Aviva Goldberg getting ready for the high ropes

Dr. Tom Blydt-Hansen and son Mac

Nurse Sandy Neustaedter

Shannon McAteer and nurses Karla Farstad and Julie Strong (from left)

Dr. Malcolm Ogborn

How We Live

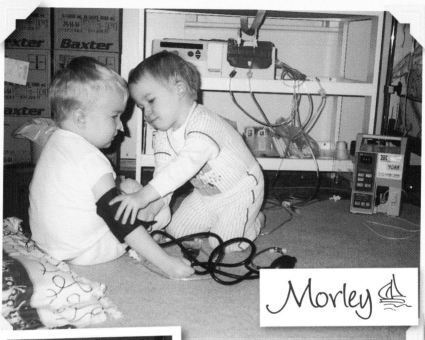

Morley ⛵

Eryk at home

Morley (right) playing with brother Jason at home

Eryk 🧸

At 10 years old, one year
before transplant

At three years old, on overnight
tube feeds for a year and a half

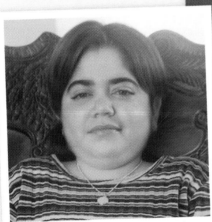

At 11 years old, two months after
transplant and taking Prednisone

Cheryl

At 17 years old (June 2000)

To Sherry and Glen. I will always see Liam in all of my dreams. I will always feel Liam blowing in the wind. I will always feel Liam touching me in the wind.

XoXoXo Love: Megan. H. + Mike

Card by Megan and Mike (with Liam and Sherry in picture)

Liam

Glen, Sherry and son Liam at home

"The best and most beautiful things in the world cannot be seen or even touched. They must be felt with the heart."

– Helen Keller
(photo by Julie Strong)

Sean and Jerry
at Kidney Camp

Janis

Janis is a 19-year-old young lady who experienced end-stage renal disease due to reflux nephropathy and was on peritoneal dialysis for a year and a half. She received a cadaveric transplant in March 2002.

My feeling, Your help

When I was a little girl
I had problems in my life,
But I did envision I'd be a woman
With talents and be strong.
Since I came in here,
I knew there was a reason why.
Because there was a problem.
But since I met you and all the other nurses,
You made me feel better.
You help me out the best you can
To get me feeling better every day.
I'm so thankful for you and all the others,
For helping me to get better.
So thanks for being the kind and nice, caring and wonderful
Nurses that you are.
I'm very glad and grateful
That you helped me through this
And I'm looking forward to the next day to meet you all again.

Author: Janis C. Bear

Written on November 15, 2002 while I was a patient on the Children's Hospital transplant ward (CK5) being treated for an episode of acute rejection of my kidney. It was written in appreciation and gratitude for the nurses on that ward who were my caregivers and supported me.

Carissa

Barry and Wendy Marmus are the parents of Carissa, an 8-year-old girl who received a kidney transplant in 2002.

The hardest part of living with kidney disease for us was the doctor visits and check-ups.

How Many Miracles?

How many miracles is anyone allowed in a lifetime? I know that two have already blessed our lives. Our first miracle was when our daughter came into our lives. We became a family through adoption when she was just over a month old. We were aware from the beginning that there were some health problems. As she grew, her kidneys were not functioning as well as they should be, but she was also growing and developing at a regular pace, so for a while we were told there was the possibility that she could grow out of her kidney problems. As her kidney function continued to decrease, it became evident that she might need a transplant someday. Just after her fourth birthday, it seemed she definitely would need a transplant someday if her condition kept progressing as it had been.

The hardest part of living with kidney disease for us was the doctor visits and check-ups. It seemed at each visit, there would be something else to have to deal with, one more hurdle to overcome as the kidney disease progressed. What made that even harder was that on a day-to-day basis, she seemed like any other busy, healthy, happy and growing child.

To look at her, you would never have known all the tests, procedures and doctor visits that she had been through. We often left the clinic feeling quite overwhelmed and devastated after being told how the disease had progressed and what may be coming next. But, as we faced and overcame each of the hurdles along the way, it also made us that much stronger, enabling us to face the next challenge. The doctors and nurses, everyone we dealt with were also always very helpful and a wealth of information. We always came in with lists of questions and then would often call back with a few more after the information we received at the check-up had a chance to sink in. Everyone involved in Carissa's care were truly healthcare professionals, always caring, extremely professional and knowledgeable.

For our family, we found the best way to live with kidney disease was to simply still live. It was a part of our lives everyday, but thankfully Carissa always felt well enough that she never missed out on doing anything she wanted to do. She loves life and has always been happy, active and outgoing. She has grown up living with kidney disease, so for her, she doesn't know anything different. Both of our families have all been there for us along the way as well, offering their love and support. We would not have got through all of this as well as we did without them. They experienced the emotional roller coaster ride with us, sharing tears of fear of the unknown and of what she would have to face as well as tears of joy and exaltation as hurdles were overcome.

Carissa was put on the transplant list in March 2002 and by late spring they were making arrangements for her to start dialysis in the fall. Once she was on the list, every time the phone would ring, our hearts would catch in our throats until we found out who was calling. We felt very constrained, having always to think about the phone before we went anywhere or did anything, but then again, we would never have wanted to miss that all important phone call. Luckily for us, we did not have to wait that long.

Our second miracle occurred in July when by the grace of God and the love and graciousness of another family, Carissa at seven and a half years of age, received her kidney transplant. It still seems so unreal because it all happened so fast, she recovered so quickly and life just keeps on going. Carissa was fully recovered and ready for the first day of school. She is so much stronger and does not tire nearly as quickly. Since the transplant, the doctor visits have been much easier to handle. It is no longer a steady progression of things getting worse each day. Instead we get to see her becoming stronger and healthier, feeling better all the time.

Carissa

Throughout all of this, I would have to say our true hero has been Carissa. She is the strongest and bravest person we know, forcing us to become stronger ourselves in order to help her deal with and understand her disease. She never let the fact that she had kidney disease be an excuse or reason for anything. She would always come in last at a race, or sometimes struggle to keep up with the other kids, but there was never a race that she wouldn't run in or an activity that she would sit out. She has always taken everything in stride, from having to endure countless tests and procedures to taking her medications. Each night before going to sleep, she says her bedtime prayers. Before the transplant, she would pray, "help me to be strong and healthy". Now, each night she says "Thank you for my new kidney, Amen." There are no words that can say it better than that.

We know there will still be bumps along the way and the possibility of other hurdles, but at least for now, the road ahead is smooth and straight.

Michelle

Michelle Virog is a 16 and a half year-old girl who received a kidney transplant from her uncle in 1995.

KIDNEY FAILURE

It all started in grade two
When I thought I just had the flu
We got a call from the hospital
Saying what I had was not good at all
I couldn't drink or even eat
Two small sips of water were my treat
They prodded and poked me
They would not let me be!
I was put in many different rooms
And I was awake when they put in the tubes
They jabbed me with a needle everyday
Trying to make sure that I would be okay
Day after day I would scream and cry
Thinking surely from all the pain I was going to die
My parents held my hand the whole time
They were about as silent as a mime
They were scared and unsure of what was going on
They had already lost their two sons
I was hooked up to all kinds of machines
My skin was the colour of an ugly green
The doctors and nurses did all that they could
They found what was wrong but still it was not good
My kidneys had failed and would never work again
That's when I knew there would be more pain
I could see the tears in their blurry eyes

Michelle

"No matter what happens we will always love you" is what they said
But they didn't know the kinds of things that were going on in my head
I had even more tubes put in my body to help me get well
"I want to go home!" is what I would yell
Finally one day I was able to go
Although they said I would still feel pretty low
I learned that there were now some forbidden foods
Bananas, oranges and chocolate too!
We were taught what to do while I was away
I would have to go through dialysis that took a couple of hours each day
I had to take pills each day and night
But I wanted to get better so I tried with all my might
Both my mom and my dad got tested to see if they were the one
But later in the year we got a call saying we had won
It was my uncle they said that matched
They said it was almost a perfect catch
I was to be pulled from school for a while
But I was so happy I could've run for a mile
We were put in rooms side by side
For once I was happy and did not cry
He was to go into surgery before me
I knew that courage was to be the key
Finally it was my turn to go down
The last words I heard were "she's out"
When I came to I barely knew what was going on
Although I was happy to know that I was not gone
When I was able to eat and sit up
I ordered chocolate milk in a cup
I had missed certain things a lot
I ate all that things that before I could not
My uncle and I were very sore
We were barely even able to walk to the door
We would have races around the hall
Not once did I ever fall
Finally it was the day when we could leave
But in the end I had been too naïve
My uncle was able to go
But when I asked they said no
My kidney had rejected me

Michelle

So once again the doctors wouldn't let me be
More tests and needles yet to come
Doesn't that sound like lots of fun?
A couple days later all was fine
Freedom was going to finally be mine
I'm still here as healthy as can be
I always have to take pills smaller than a pea
I've lasted seven years and won't stop now
I've become stronger and here's how:
I had family and friends to help me through
And now I'm telling my story to you
Remember to live life to the fullest
And always try to do your best
What's in the future no one knows
So treat it just like a beautiful red rose

- By Michelle Virog

Jesse

Jesse McMullen, was a 17-year-old when he received a kidney transplant. He was diagnosed with Alport's Syndrome at the age of 8.

> ... it was a big surprise to see my room all changed around so that there was room for my dialysis machine.

I was diagnosed with Alport's Syndrome at age eight. Being young, I had no idea what it was, and never asked about it. To me, it was just another trip to the doctor.

As I got older, around 13, I had to start on medication. That's when I kind of started to think about it, and wonder what was going to happen in the long term.

It never really bothered me physically until I was about fifteen, and had to start taking more medication. That's when I started to get headaches in the morning and then felt really nauseous. I usually only ate a piece of toast for breakfast because that's all my stomach could handle.

I had what was called Restless Leg Syndrome, and couldn't sit still for very long. My legs would hurt unless I was standing or walking around. With any physical activity I would get bad leg cramps and my legs were losing strength.

Then at age seventeen, I had my dialysis catheter put into my abdomen. It was in January just after my birthday. I spent one and a half weeks in the hospital recovering from my surgery. When I arrived for the surgery, their intention was to put the catheter in just as a precaution. They didn't intend to use it for sure, because I was having a kidney transplant in March, but then my kidney function dropped drastically after surgery. My dialysis started four hours after surgery. The dialysis was very painful for the first week I was in the hospital. The painkillers I was getting didn't seem to help at all.

When I arrived at home, it was a big surprise to see my room all changed around so that there was room for my dialysis machine. The amount of supplies took up a big portion of our basement. With dialysis at home it was a huge change in my life. I had to be hooked up to my machine nine hours a night while I slept. It was only six nights a week so I got one night off a week. Each day I would set up supplies for that night, which usually took about half an hour. I hardly ever had to do it on my own because my mom helped with it. My dad didn't get the teaching my mom and I got at the hospital.

Then when the time came for the surgery, after my dad went through all the testing to be a donor, and my mom was pulling her hair out getting everything at home ready, we all went to Winnipeg on March 30th. We arrived, got our rooms, and had our IVs put in. At about nine o'clock our doctor came and told us we couldn't have the surgery, because in the final crossmatch they found a flaw. So we went back home again to wait. They sent the blood away to Atlanta to get checked. After about three weeks at home, they found out the transplant was a go again. So we set a new date for June 1st.

The surgery went well and the new kidney worked almost right away. I was pretty sore, but my dad was worse I think, because he is older. My mom was drained from running back and forth from my room to my dad's. The stay in the hospital was good and the nurses were nice. I was discharged from the hospital in one week

We moved into an apartment across the street for six more weeks, seeing the doctor almost every day. I had to be at the hospital at eight o'clock each morning.

Now I'm home, feel great, and don't even remember not feeling well.

Jesse

Terrance

Terry McNabb is a 13-year-old boy who has been on dialysis in the past. He received a kidney transplant in October 1999.

When I got my kidney I was feeling great.

When I was a little boy I was very sick. But, when I got my kidney I was feeling good. But let me tell you when you don't have a kidney it feels awful. You are sick most of the time, you have no energy and you are not hungry. You also get puffed up. You also had to get fed by a feeding tube. But, when you have a kidney things are different. You can run and play, you can eat more and you have more energy. When I got my kidney I was feeling great. I could run and play. I could eat lots, like french fries, rice, peas and other foods. I like to run, jog and play ball. My favorite sport is basketball. I can get two out of five 3 - pointers. I also like to play hockey and other sports.

I live in LLB with my family. They are Tanis, Neal and Aunt Donna. It is cool to live with them. I like to play catch with Neal and Tanis.

The End.
Terry McNabb

Terry McNabb won an award for his school essays on Recycling as well as War and Peace. When asked if he would like to submit any stories or drawings for this project, he chose to share these essays.

Please Recycle

I think everyone should recycle anything that they can because it helps the streets, community, province and country and the earth. We should start recycling everything we can so that it doesn't fill the garbage dumps all over the world. Besides that, it can help you out by getting money for what you recycle. You give and you get back – you earn what you work for!!

We should get rid of all the gases and the oils so that the atmosphere will be clean again. We should use solar power instead of gas so that we don't poison our atmosphere.

You should use a compost because it can help your garden revive. It is good for the soil.

We should reuse the bags that we use for lunch. Even though we don't get money for it, we should reuse whatever we can.

Please recycle because it is all "Too Good To Waste"

Do You Want War or Peace?

Soldiers came from different countries and different towns. They fought for all people and for different reasons.

Please remember all the veterans and the people who fought in the war. Today, on November 11, 2003 we wear a poppy to help remember what the veterans did for us.

I feel that war is bad because it just kills a generation of old people, young people and middle aged people. I don't think that war is good because no one ever wins it. Once you start a war, it is hard to stop it because people have anger inside of them.

Peace is good because nobody gets hurt or killed. We should be like children because they work and reason things out. I love peace because it doesn't take any members away from you family.

When our soliders came back from the war, they came back with scars, not only on their bodies but also in their minds and spirits. We hurt Mother Nature, the soil and the crops when we drop bombs.

Let's Stop War Forever!

Holly

Holly is a 17-year-old girl who has had two failed transplants and is currently on hemodialysis. Terry Dowse has been Holly's foster mother since she was 10-years-old.

Holly's Interview

When I was told I had kidney disease/ needed dialysis/needed a transplant…
"I didn't really care. I was really sick and I just wanted to feel better. I don't know. I was just really sick. I was scared of needles and I didn't want it at first. My foster mother at the time, helped me deal with the diagnosis. At first I didn't want anybody to know. Now I tell people only if they ask questions. They think I am lucky because I don't have to go pee all the time but I tell them, "believe me, you're much better off going to the bathroom always." They have no idea."

I felt sad, scared and alone.

Friends and acquaintances treat me differently now that I have kidney disease and dialysis in that…
"They care more about me."

What I hate most about having kidney disease is…
"The diet and not being able to eat what I want or what I love and too many appointments. No time to have a life and friends."

When I stayed in the hospital…

"I felt sad, scared and alone. The worst part about being in the hospital was being alone. My favorite parts were watching TV, videos and CH TV (a closed circuit television station within Children's Hospital). My stay could be better if the food was tastier and I wasn't so sick."

My advice to another kid about living with kidney disease, would be…

"To take care of yourself – take all your medications, eat properly, stick to the diet, ask lots of questions if you are not sure about something and live each day to the fullest."

When I have dialysis, I feel…

"When I'm on dialysis I feel fine. When I have a lot of fluid to take off, then it starts to hurt. But all in all it feels fine.

When you are waiting for a transplant, you feel…

"Like it will take forever and when it finally comes, it is such a surprise. I don't know who donated the kidneys that were transplanted in me. I think that these people were awesome to think about another life in need. I just wish that it could have worked for me because both of those transplants failed. My fear about another transplant is that it is not going to work. I will miss out on all the fun things my family is doing. My fear of dialysis is that I will get a horrible infection."

Terry's Story

I didn't know Holly when she was first sick. I know that she was 9, almost 10 years old, when she was diagnosed with kidney disease and her kidneys completely failed within six months. I met Holly at Children's Hospital when she was first put on peritoneal dialysis. She was a tiny 10-year-old, happy and outgoing on the outside and yet very sick, facing life alone with a life threatening disease. My heart went out to her and because I was coping with loss and feeling empty on the inside, Holly was the answer to my prayers.

Kidney disease has totally changed my life. We live from appointment to appointment. We take every moment and run with it. People and time are very precious commodities, not to be taken for granted. Time is a gift and we live in this moment. I've learned so much about the human body, medications and diet. It's sometimes overwhelming.

> When your child is sick you feel very fragmented, like you don't know what you should do next and there's always so much to do.

It's very hard on the family, living with kidney disease. The moments you have to spend together are few and far between. Yet when those moments come, they are awesome. When your child is sick you feel very fragmented, like you don't know what you should do next and there's always so much to do. You feel like your going to break and like everyone's angry because you have no time to finish anything properly. We've learned to do the best we can and pick up and help where and when we can. Kidney disease has taught us to be less critical, more loving and caring. Life without kidney disease would be normal.

If I could give another family advice about living with kidney disease, it would be live today. You don't know what tomorrow will bring and you can't change what happened yesterday. Love your child but don't coddle them. Help them with their medications, diet, appointments, homework, etc. but don't take over for them. This is their life and we must let them live it. Laugh lots and more if you can. Sing all those old silly songs. Be strong and rigid when you have to but let loose and have fun as often as you can. Live – make happy memories.

We learned about kidney disease from the medical staff in pediatric nephrology and from reading the materials they sent home with us.

My feelings about dialysis are wow – dialysis is life and without dialysis and all the doctors and nurses that work with us there would be no life for my little girl. If Holly got a transplant, one that worked, it would mean an almost normal life. My fears about Holly being on dialysis is that one day it won't work or she'll get a bad infection or they'll run out of veins to access. My fears about transplant are that it will fail and Holly will die.

Holly

Waiting for a transplant seems to take forever. Holly had her first transplant about one and half years after being put on dialysis. We were so excited, living moment by moment, just waiting for the word that "yes, it works." When the transplant failed, we were crushed. Holly received another transplant two and half years later. It hung on for four months, leaving her at death's door. It was so heart wrenching and depressing but she managed to pull herself back together again. Something like Humpty Dumpty.

I am so thankful to those people who donated those kidneys to Holly. I think it takes a wonderful person to take the focus off self and give such a precious gift so someone else can live. I had asked about giving one of my own kidneys to Holly because we are the same blood type. She is not mine by birth and I have a biological son with only one good working kidney so the doctors suggested I keep mine for him if need be. So we live day by day and pray that God keeps us healthy and happy and when the next transplant comes that it will be a perfect fit. They say the third times a charm, right?!

Holly has had to face many trials in her life. She has faced death many times and survived. I'm proud to say that Holly is my hero if only for the simple reason that she gets up every morning and tries her best. I love Holly. She has taught me so much about life.

Amanda

Amanda Haines is a 19-year-old girl, who received a kidney transplant from her mother. She wrote these poems to her mom and dad, Patricia and Scott.

This poem is dedicated to my mother,
We have a bond that is like no other.
She gave me a remarkable gift in my time of need,
Everyone would say she did a tremendous deed.

She gave me a part of her for which I could never thank enough,
My dad and her were there through every time, rough and tough.
From now on I will call her my one true best friend,
When I was sick, my mom and dad were the only ones who had a hand to lend.

I know we still have our good times and bad,
But I know in my heart, we can't ever stay mad.
I feel like I can always and forever say,
Our bond is getting stronger each and every day

In the future I know it will always stay the same,
Because our bind will be so strong, there would be nothing to blame.
Our love for each other will never end,
And we will always be the closest of friends.

To close this I would like to say,
A little thing if I may,
I love you, Mom with all my heart and forever.
I thank for all you've done, take this with you forever and ever.

This poem is written for you, Dad, to tell you how much I care,
I want to thank you for cheering me up every time you were there.
Without you, Dad, my life would be incomplete,
I need you there to help me on my feet.

You helped me out every time I thought life was not fair,
I can see in your eyes how much you really care.
When I was sick you were always by my side,
Forever and always, not letting my emotions hide.

You taught me well day by day,
You did an excellent job, I must say.
I've grown up, tried to do everything right,
And I've learned not to give up without a fight.

You and Mom do all that you can do,
I bet in the future, we will be stuck forever like glue.
You always and forever say,
Never give up and live your life each day.

To end this poem I have something to tell you dad,
You are my father and I am so glad.
I love you forever with all my heart,
And I thank you from the very start.

Amanda Haines
Age: 16
Kidney Transplant

Sean is a 12-year-old boy whose treatment included peritoneal dialysis. Sean's dad, Bob, donated a kidney to his son in 2002.

Everyone would ask me how the dialysis was making me feel.

My name is Sean Dusko and I was 12 years old when I found out I had kidney disease. When I found out I was kind of scared and a little upset. I didn't know what would happen next. We found out through some testing that was being done on my legs and hips because they were very painful. The first doctor we saw was a bone specialist and I had slipped capital femur, which meant my legs were slipping off my hips; I had pins put in and every thing seemed fine for a few months, but then it wasn't helping my legs after a few months so we started doing more blood tests and found out that my kidneys weren't working. This is when we went to see the doctors at the Renal Clinic.

We met with the doctor and he explained to my mom and dad and me about my kidney disease. Soon after we started treatment and I had a catheter put in my stomach so that I would be ready for dialysis, which I started in February. I really didn't like doing dialysis, it was hard to sleep, and I had to go to bed early, even on weekends. It was also a lot of work for all of us.

Dialysis made me feel better. Everyone would ask me how the dialysis was making me feel. I would tell them that it helps me lots but that it is a lot of work and time that I must do this every night. My friends and people were always very supportive of my situation and worried a lot about me.

I have been in the hospital many times since I first started feeling sick. The first couple of times I was very nervous and didn't know what was going to happen. My mom and dad explained to me but I was still scared a little. Even after I knew what was going to happen I was still a little nervous. The hospital was ok, and I had my own room, but I am also deaf and the TV's in the room don't have closed captioning on them. The nurse's and helpers at the hospital were very nice and they found me a TV with closed captioning so I could enjoy watching TV while I stayed at the hospital.

In October, almost a year after finding out about my disease, I would have my transplant with my dad's kidney. I was happy that I would not need dialysis anymore, but I was also very nervous about the operation. My dad and I were lucky to share the same room at the hospital, but I wouldn't see him for two days after the operation because I would be with the other nurse's who would take care of me after the operation. I was very sick after the operation, and uncomfortable. I threw up a couple of times and the doctor's and nurse's were very helpful and by Saturday afternoon I was feeling good enough to go back to my room with my Dad. It was a lot of work for everyone and I am very happy that everything worked out great, but it wasn't easy. The worst part for me was the IV's that I had to have. I am very happy that my Dad was a match and that I now have a working kidney and I am doing well.

Dad's Story

Sean's diagnosis, as he said, wasn't straightforward. He first started complaining about pains in his legs and hips when he was 12 years old. We sort of wrote it off as growing pains for a few months until it seemed to get so bad that he looked like an old man with arthritis getting off the school bus and even sitting in a chair. We were finally sent to a bone specialist and found that his legs were slipping off his hips, something that happens to some boys in their growing years from 11 to 14. It was pretty serious and he was admitted to hospital where he had pins inserted in his hips and legs to keep them from slipping any further. The operation went smoothly and his legs started to return to a normal state. He started feeling much better and the pain was gone so he said.

We continued going to the bone specialist and he kept measuring his leg curvature and for the first while it kept getting smaller and seemed to be growing back in the right direction, as before his legs seemed to be growing outward. After a couple of more visits to the specialist he noticed that they had stopped getting better and kind of reversed themselves so that they were again growing outward.

We were sent for some blood tests and then sent to the Renal Clinic to see a Kidney Doctor. This is where we first found out that Sean's kidney function was at 20% and dropping and that his kidneys' weren't functioning.

For me, finding out what was causing the problems for my son was a relief, the pain of him having kidney disease was devastating. Holding back the tears and setting into another unknown area of life (we had also discovered Sean was deaf when he was 1-1/2 years old) I told him that whatever he had to go through to get better I would be beside him and we would work through it no matter what.

Now on a new journey we started learning about kidney disease, about dialysis, diet, medicine, and transplant. Being a dad, all I wanted to know was if I could give him one of my kidneys and help him have some sort of normal life.

In the next couple of months, we learned a lot about kidney disease and dialysis and Sean was fitted with a catheter for dialysis. The medicine was delivered (WOW), lots of it and we brought home the dialysis machine and started him on treatment every night. As a treatment dialysis works wonders and he was feeling better right away, but the restrictions that dialysis put on Sean and us made a

For me, finding out what was causing the problems for my son was a relief, the pain of him having kidney disease was devastating.

Sean

transplant seem like the only way to go. Ten hours a day on a machine, absolute cleanliness to make sure of no infections, set up every night and cleaning the catheter every other day, not to mention the medicine, put an incredible amount of stress on our lives.

I began testing for a living donor match soon after we started dialysis. After about six months of testing, I was cleared to be a living donor. Now we would wait for a time to have the transplant done and hope that everything would work. A little more stress to throw on the pile but this one was well worth the wait.

The wait for the transplant seemed like forever but in reality it was less than a year. Neither of us knew what to expect, probably me less than Sean, he had been in for surgery a couple of times by now, but I had never had a type of surgery in my life. The day came and the transplant was completed successfully. Other than a lot of tiredness and some discomfort I was up and walking in a couple of days, but my transplanted kidney in Sean seemed to take a little longer to get kick started. By Saturday, Sean was back with me in the room and doing much better. Thanks to all the doctors and nurses, and everyone at the clinic, the whole process went effortlessly for us.

I have to admit going through the surgery, with all the anxiety, waiting, testing, and not knowing what surgery would be like was very stressful. There were lots of questions about how I would feel. Would it be different minus one kidney? Would Sean accept the kidney? But after going through it all, I would do it again for anyone I could.

Since he has had his new kidney Sean's life is that which a child's should be. Other than taking his medication he is living a normal life and has the opportunity to do the things a child should be able to do: Swimming, sleepovers, not worrying about doing his dialysis, and feeling so much better.

For families going through the pain of kidney disease (my thoughts are with you) and if there is any chance of being a donor, be there for them, it is truly a gift!

Jasmine

Jasmine Nemetchek was a 14-year-old girl, whose treatments have included peritoneal dialysis, hemodialysis and a transplant. She was diagnosed with Schimke's Immuno-osseus Dysplasia at the age of 7. Jasmine passed away in April 2002.

When I was seven years old I was diagnosed with a rare genetic disease called Schimke's Immuno-osseus Dysplasia. This disease affects my kidneys, bones and white blood cells.

After my eighth birthday, I went into kidney failure and began peritoneal dialysis. I was on this type of dialysis for three years until I had a really bad infection, and had to switch to hemodialysis.

During my three and half years on dialysis I also had to be tube fed and went through thirty surgeries. I have learned many things going through so much pain and uncertainty.

Above all, I have learned to stay close to God because He is the only one who can change things. Secondly, I have learned that you need to love and appreciate your family.

I have a lot to be thankful for. On September 17th, 1998 I had a kidney transplant with the help of my mom, who donated one of her kidneys. I have been doing well, but still get sick with flus and viruses.

I would like to thank the many doctors and nurses who took great care of me when I was in the Children's Hospital, especially one doctor and nurse in particular for all their special care.

I write this in memory of a small boy I met and spent time with in the Children's Hospital. His name is Morley. Morley went to heaven in September of 1995 and I will never forget him or his family.

Morley

Steve and Betsy are the parents of 6-year-old Morley. Morley had chronic renal failure and received peritoneal dialysis and a kidney transplant prior to his death in September 1995.

The Lord is my shepherd, I shall lack nothing."
(Psalms 23:1)

Fourteen years ago, my best friend, my mother, was diagnosed with cancer. Two months later she went to be with the Lord.

My thoughts often drift back to my High School years. Every day when I walked in the door, my mom and I would talk. She enthusiastically told me about her garden and sewing circle and I gabbed about school, friends, boys and youth. We had an unusually close-knit relationship. After I graduated and got a job in Blumenort, she waited for me to come home for the weekends and some Friday nights we talked until late. We were bosom friends as *Anne of Green Gables* puts it.

Only one year after Steve and I got married, she went home to be with the Lord. Words are much too shallow to explain how much I missed her, especially after the birth of each of our three children. I again needed her, like never before, when our oldest son, Morley, became chronically ill eight years ago and was called to his eternal home two years later.

The Lord reminded me "I can do everything through him who give me strength." (Philippians 4:13)

Morley was four years old when he began to cough uncontrollably, but only at night. Possibly, we thought, he was allergic to his feather pillow or maybe the stuffed fox in his room. Then he started waking up with puffy eyes. I was blissfully ignorant. I did not realize that Morley's coughing and his puffy eyes were symptoms of kidney failure. The fluid that pooled around his eyes at night was distributed throughout the rest of his body within the first few hours of the day, the coughing subsided in the morning and so I was not particularly worried. In fact Morley had had a bedwetting problem but the last morning before he was thrown into the hospital for two and a half months, Morley woke up dry. I was elated. I had noticed though, that Morley seemed unusually lethargic. This was reason to have him checked out. My roller coaster of emotions plummeted when a Steinbach doctor told me Morley's kidneys were failing. We were ordered to go straight to the Children's Hospital without even stopping at home. Jason was two years old and Terri, six months old at this time. I explained that I simply must arrange for their Grandma to take them with her. I knew Steve would be coming home to allow for her to tend to her other commitment. I had no intentions of letting her leave without taking my two babies with her so Steve would be free to drive Morley and me to Winnipeg.

This was the beginning of countless blood tests, finger pokes, blood pressure checks, IV's, biopsies etc.

Steve and I were naïve and anxious at the onset of Morley's illness. The unknown bared heavy on our hearts. The Nephrologists reassured us that Morley's life was not threatened and there was a good chance that his kidneys could be saved. One evening when two friends came to visit, I told them I had peace knowing Morley would not die and all I was concerned about was that he would never need dialysis and a transplant.

It took three biopsies before Morley's disease was diagnosed. I will never forget that dark and cold evening. I was fighting the stomach flu when one of the doctors walked into our room and gave me the news. He explained the disease, the type of treatment they were going to try with huge doses of IV Prednisone and all the dreaded side effects of this drug. I felt numbed! It hit like a bombshell that this was no ten-day prescription. The doctor had been talking years and still there was NO guarantee Morley's kidneys would function normally. I wanted some sort of a guarantee! I had nowhere else to run except into God's eternal arms and hide there. I found myself helplessly clinging to Him and putting my trust in Him for whatever the bleak future would bring. Steve and I couldn't keep going in our own strength. We desperately needed supernatural strength.

Morley's body, however, did not respond to Prednisone and in less than a month from when he was diagnosed, we met with one of the specialists to hear him explain that dialysis was inevitable and a future transplant was discussed as well. Morley's condition deteriorated rapidly and that same week a dialysis catheter was put in and only hours after surgery, I watched him get hooked up to a machine, which would be his buddy for the next two years.

My dreams of becoming a nurse were being fulfilled in ways that I had never imagined. After Christmas, my training began. I learned how to do dialysis, dressing changes, insert NG tubes, give EPO needles, do blood pressure checks and all about the meds. I often felt very overwhelmed by it all but the Lord renewed my strength one hour at a time.

Looking back, the summer before the transplant is a very memorable summer. Considering Morley had kidney disease, he did very well and we carried on a near normal lifestyle. We went swimming numerous times. We purchased a battery operated 4-wheeler for Morley which was his pride and joy that summer.

> Morley and I were looking forward to transplant day with great anticipation. We were counting down the number of dressing changes, needles and the number of times we would have to put an NG tube in.

Morley and I were looking forward to transplant day with great anticipation. We were counting down the number of dressing changes, needles and the number of times we would have to put an NG tube in. Steve, who would be the donor, was a little more apprehensive. But the evening prior to this major event, we all felt pretty lighthearted and we laughed a lot. We had explained to Morley that there would be pain and discomfort involved. We also played it up that the end result would be well worth it and Morley excitedly talked about how he would enjoy eating all of his favorite foods again.

Morley's transplanted kidney began to make urine at about 3:00 the morning following surgery and I have never been so excited to see pee. For seven days it seemed as though we would just breeze right through. Then exactly one week after the transplant, complications set in from which Morley never recovered.

Morley was transferred to the Intensive Care Unit after an emergency operation to clean out the blood clots that were blocking the blood flow through the kidney. When I was allowed to go in and see Morley, it seemed like death was hanging in the air. He was hooked up to a respirator and had drug induced paralysis. He lay there, lifeless and unresponsive. The nurses encouraged me to touch him and talk to him. They told me they had noticed that when Morley felt my touch and heard my voice, he responded and that many times his blood pressure and heart rate went down. So I read to him, we listened to music, I held his hand in mine and I prayed out loud with him.

God picked us both up in His strong arms and carried us. I felt completely enveloped in His love! Many times during this stretch of three weeks in ICU, I felt as though God had allowed my oldest child and me to come with Him on a long journey. I felt special! I felt like singing as I walked down the long corridors on my way to get coffee.

Morley, while he was immunosuppressed, got an infection in his blood. Possibly this was from the malfunctioning kidney and the kidney had to be removed immediately! One of our doctors told Steve, Morley's life was on the edge of a cliff and every minute counted. I knelt beside Morley's bed just before they wheeled him out to the operating room and taking his hand, I prayed that God would keep him strong. I felt so incredibly helpless. Even though Morley was on the respirator and heavily sedated, I wanted him to know I was there and that Jesus would go with him wherever he went. Morley's nurse, with tears in her eyes came around to my side of the bed, put her arm around me and prayed, "And please help Morley's mom to be strong too". Morley survived three major operations in less than three weeks but without a working kidney.

Steve and I were just thankful that we still had Morley with us.

After two months in the hospital during this admission, Morley was discharged home on December 23, just in time for Christmas. He was very weak and needed to be carried like an infant, his blood pressure was elevated, he had diarrhea and was constantly throwing up. I felt emotionally and physically drained. I have to confess, I screamed at God more than once and I have had to plead His forgiveness many times. Morley could often sense my frustration and he would try to cheer me up by singing 'Jesus Loves Me' or by reminding me that Jesus, myself and him were on a team and we could do anything. Other times he apologized for the mess that he had made.

Morley regained some strength and he proudly learned to walk again but he experienced a feeling of nausea all the time. Often when he was driving his 4-wheeler, he would stop, get off and throw up, then continue driving. I would try to keep everyone's morale up by having picnics just outside the front door and by filling the wading pool with water, pretending we were at the beach. Sometimes we would invite friends to our beach parties. But always, we had to have the puke bowl ready and the lounger set up nearby because Morley tired very quickly.

One morning in June, Morley was rushed to the Children's Hospital by ambulance after I found him in a coma. His sugar levels had reached over 100. Once again he was taken to the Intensive Care Unit, hooked up to a respirator and sedated. We prayed that Morley would just be able to go to Heaven to be with Jesus. He was diagnosed as having diabetes, which was severely complicated by his dialysis since the fluid used in dialysis has high concentrations of sugar.

It was during this admission that Morley was also diagnosed with an underlying, very complex cell disorder, which had initially caused kidney failure and now diabetes and could lead to other body organs shutting down one by one. This came as a real blow, for Steve and I had renewed hope and were gunghoe on doing a combination kidney and pancreas transplant. God was ultimately in control. We understood that there was nothing more we could do. We made a decision, at this time, not to have Morley put on life support again, should another crisis arise and to commit him to the Lord.

In fall, Morley's dialysis stopped working for him and fluids and wastes began to build up. On September 12, 1995, Morley let go of our hands and took hold of Jesus' hand and they crossed the finish line together. Morley died peacefully while rocking in my arms.

After two years of intense struggling, "Death has been swallowed up in victory." (1 Corinthians 15:54b). No more dialysis and tube feeding, no more needles, pokes, scans, x-rays, blood pressure checks and meds. No more moaning and groaning in discomfort and pain. No more diarrhea and nausea. Morley has finished the race.

Morley has achieved an award that everyone of us is still striving for. At times I have this awesome feeling well up inside of me and flood my entire being. I am so proud of Morley, the way he heroically ran the race. He beat us. He has won his eternal medal.

For the first year it was this feeling of victory that helped me cope with the large void that comes with separation. The race had been so intense that death brought an aspect of relief. Don't get me wrong. My arms ached to give Morley a hug, to hold him and rock him and to hear his voice. But we had been watching Morley merely waste away and separation brought momentary relief.

Since then I have had to struggle with loneliness, discouragement and depression. Instead of running to Jesus and finding companionship, encouragement and strength in Him, I often unfairly blame Steve for being insensitive and preoccupied with our business.

The Lord has to constantly remind me "He is my shepherd, I shall lack nothing". (Psalm 23:1) He is all that I need. Only the Lord, not my mom, my children or my husband, is able to fill my heart with "The peace of God, which transcends all understanding..." (Philippians 4:7a)

In my desperate search for joy, I often place unrealistically high expectations on Steve and this has caused a real strain on our marriage. I have underlined this verse in my Bible. "Find rest, O my soul, in God alone; my expectation comes from him". (Psalm 62:5) The Lord is not through with me yet. I am slow to learn. He is trying to teach me that He is everything I need. When I'm feeling alone or misunderstood, I throw myself into God's everlasting arms of love and hide there for a while. "The eternal God is your refuge, and underneath are the everlasting arms." (Deuteronomy 33:27a)

Some days, for every step forward, I take two steps back. But the Lord encourages me to press on. "Not that I have already obtained all this, or have already been made perfect, but I press on to take hold of that for which Christ Jesus took hold of me. But one thing I do: Forgetting what is behind and straining toward what is ahead." (Philippians 3:12 & 13b)

"Therefore, since we are surrounded by such a great cloud of witnesses, let us throw off everything that hinders and the sin that so easily entangles, and let us run with perseverance the race marked out for us. Let us fix our eyes on Jesus...." (Hebrews 12:1 & 2a)

With Morley sitting on his Grandma's lap and the two of them cheering me on from the grandstands of heaven, I will run with perseverance the race marked out for me. I will keep my eyes fixed on Jesus, my Shepherd. Thank-you!

Robert

Robert is an 11-year-old boy who received a kidney transplant in 2000. The interview with Robert and his mother, Donna Burghart, was in December 2002.

Robert's Interview

"I almost fell 'cause the kidney was heavy – it came from a man. In about one year I started running and now I can run really fast!"

Robert doesn't remember being told he had kidney disease because he was 5 years old. He does remember how he felt about getting a transplant (in late 2000); he felt "scared" and said that it "hurt." Robert describes dialysis as "boring, weird & noisy; it takes a long time in the morning." "Sunday was fun, 'cause I didn't have to get hooked up." He says his friends ask him questions about his portacath & gastrostomy and he tells them "I have the tube because my kidney doesn't work and I tell them I have a feeding tube." "One kid said it was cool, but it's not cool 'cause you have to get hooked up. Once a kid touched it and pulled on it." "Kids ask me how it feels and I tell them, it's kinda weird." Robert says his classmates don't tease him, "they really care about me." He thinks people do treat him differently. He and his mom remember her worrying about him getting hurt when he was playing, for about the first year after his transplant.

Robert and his mom laughed when asked if he had ever been in hospital – "about 20 times" he said! He says the best thing about being in hospital is sleeping, and the worst thing is the needles. His idea about how to make hospital stays better for kids is to have computers right in the rooms. (He was in isolation during this interview.) When asked who has helped him the most with his kidney disease, Robert replied: The Kidney Doctors; they're all my favorite doctors!"

Robert's advice to other kids who need a kidney transplant: "It's not going to be that bad. It wasn't as bad as I thought it would be." He felt "happy" not to be on dialysis anymore. Robert has a vivid memory of his first "practice walk" after surgery. "I almost fell 'cause the kidney was heavy – it came from a man. In about one year I started running and now I can run really fast!"

Donna's Interview

Donna and her partner Andy Captain adopted Robert when he was very young (he is Andy's grandson.) They were living in Edmonton with Donna's teenage daughter when Robert developed flu like symptoms. He was given an antibiotic and sent home. When he didn't improve they took him back to the doctor and the dose was increased. He woke up in the middle of that night crying. Robert's face and hands were swollen and his belly and behind his ears were "blue." They took him to the Emergency Department and Donna remembers that being a "terrible experience." Robert was "screaming in pain, 12-14 doctors examined him and we were there for 7 hours." Finally Robert was transferred to a children's hospital and "that's when all the kidney treatment started, and I stayed 24 hours a day for the first week." The next week Robert had 3 cardiac arrests. Donna remembers him being in Intensive Care and the doctor telling her there was nothing more they could do. "They started to unhook him from the machinery, but then I felt him squeeze my hand. I said doctor, doctor, look!" They continued treatment and he slowly began to recover.

Robert recalled a dream from that experience: "I had a dream when my heart stopped. It was dark everywhere, then I saw a bright light. I saw a man walk inside the bright light. So I went for a peek and saw a word that said Heaven. I decided to go back."

Donna remembers the process of accepting that Robert's kidneys had failed as being long and difficult. She said there was a long wait to see if they would start working again. "We had to catheterize him for 8 months." "It was very, very hard to accept his kidneys were gone. We went through a series of adjustments. We both had to learn dialysis. It was not hard to learn (Robert was in the hospital in Edmonton for one year) but it was very scary when we took him home and we were there alone without any nurses around." Donna remembers that as a time when she wanted so badly to look after "that little boy" that she tried to become a "super mom" and eventually had a breakdown she became so exhausted. Fortunately Donna's partner and her physician realized what was happening and told her she must take a break and go away to have a rest for three whole days and was told no one would answer the phone if she called home to check on Robert!

She has a vivid memory of being in the grocery store shortly after Robert was discharged and searching for packages and tins with no salt and sugar. She ended up in tears at the check out, feeling like this was going to be impossible. Robert's father Andy coped better according to Donna: "Andy did really well with it, he was very confident, he was my rock." Donna describes feeling like a nurse without the training. "We had to weigh him every day, take his blood pressure, monitor his heart with a stethoscope and learn how to do this all in three weeks. I didn't stop to think this would be a life situation, I thought he'd get better. It was part of my denial. Now I can accept he may need another transplant, that he will have diabetes all his life; I can accept what comes along."

The 3 a.m. phone call from the doctor telling the family a kidney had become available for Robert, came after they had moved to Swan River, a community about 6 hours from Winnipeg. Robert was now getting his care at Winnipeg's Children's Hospital and they had just returned by plane from a trip to the hospital that day. They discovered the dialysis machine was not working and spoke to the company in British Columbia who would deliver one the next day. Little did they know what was in store

"I try to keep things balanced but it's hard."

the following day! Donna said she was "scared and happy at the same time" after the Doctor called. She described the day of surgery as "a long eight hours!" One month after his transplant Donna was admitted to HSC with a lung clot and was hospitalized for a whole month. She remembers visiting Robert in her housecoat.

About seven months ago Donna enrolled in Diabetes Education Training and on January 18, 2003 she will graduate with marks ranging from 83 – 93%. She hopes to work part-time helping the many people who have diabetes. She took the training "to learn more, to get out and to meet people. I'm glad I took it. I can prepare healthy meals now, I learned about hypoglycemia and next we'll learn an exercise program." Donna feels she has learned a huge life lesson from everything she has been through with Robert and his health. She does not plan to work full time because she knows the amount of time his condition requires from their family. "I try to keep things balanced but it's hard." Donna's advice to other parents: "Don't try to do everything yourself, take advantage of the help that is available."

Cheryl ☀ ～

Irene and Ron Simoens are the parents of Cheryl, an 18-year-old girl with Cystinosis who received a kidney transplant in 1995.

Our daughter's name is Cheryl Lynn Simoens, born December 2, 1983, weighing 7 lbs, 5oz. Cheryl's family consists of mother, Irene, father, Ronald, one brother, Michael (7 years older), sister Christine (15 years older, and a much closer sister Lori, only 23 months older.

Cheryl was a healthy baby and gained weight quickly. In August of 1984, at eight months of age, she had flu-like symptoms, losing weight, not eating, being listless and constantly bringing up anything she ate. I took her to our family doctor, who told us to give her plenty of fluids. Cheryl showed no improvement so I took her back. I told him that she kept bringing up after drinking milk, thinking she might have been allergic to cows milk. Switching to goats milk didn't change anything. Because she was drinking so much water and wetting her diapers more than the other children ever did, I was concerned that perhaps it might be diabetes or kidney problems. I knew that both of these conditions cause a person to drink more than normal. One night when I gave her a bottle of milk, she threw her bottle across the room demanding water. She was about ten months old then and only drank from a glass during the day, but that night when I gave her the glass of water, she drank like there was no tomorrow. I took her back to our family doctor and insisted that there was definitely something wrong with her. That afternoon we saw a child specialist who diagnosed her as extremely dehydrated and lethargic. We were immediately admitted to St. Boniface Hospital.

Many questions were asked and answers were given regarding family history on our kidney problems. We told them about Ron's sister, who had two boys who seemed healthy at birth, but later developed a kidney disease called Cystinosis. It is a rare and inherited kidney disorder, and Ron and I both had to be carriers. Our reaction was immediately one of shock and disbelief. We knew what was ahead for both Cheryl and the rest of the family. That evening Ron's sister and her husband met us at the hospital and said in tears, "Cheryl is the daughter we never had."

There were days when I would stand at the kitchen counter over medicine bottles and cry.

They lost their two sons to Cystinosis, one in 1973 at the age of eight, and one in 1977 at the age of eleven. Kidney transplants at that time didn't offer a viable cure.

Ron and I had to put our life into God's hands and deal with the situation, one day at a time. I remember when my sister came to visit us in the hospital. She was very sympathetic and willing to help in any way she could. She was about to start crying for us and I told her to please not do that because once I started I might not have been able to deal with it.

Five days later we were sent home with many medications and we prepared for the difficult days ahead of us. She had various medications including iron because she was anemic. We gave her a lot of tender, loving care.

Cheryl

It was not easy at times. There were days when I would stand at the kitchen counter over medicine bottles and cry. Feeling sorry for myself, I was often tired because I had to wake up during the night two or three times to give her water and change her diapers. Diapers (cloth in those days) and all of her bedding had to be washed daily. There was a lot of work preparing special diet foods, and giving medication four times a day, and she was still bringing up a lot. I had helped my sister-in-law with her two boys, and so I was aware of what was ahead

Even though Cheryl was so sick, she had a great disposition, never cried, but just sat there, looking lethargic, watching her siblings come and go. She wouldn't play much and dragged herself around the house to see where the action was.

In February of 1984, Cheryl was 14 months old and weighed only 19 lbs, and wasn't feeling very well. She was quite sick with what we thought was the flu. I remember my father holding her in his arms, while I was preparing myself to go see the doctor with her, for yet another visit because she was so limp and lifeless. She kept closing her eyes. It seemed that the only thing she was aware of was that we were all caring for her.

Our family physician examined her briefly, and realizing how dehydrated she was, immediately phoned the Children's Hospital. Cheryl was rushed there by ambulance. She was so dehydrated and her electrolytes were so out of balance that they had to work on her all night. Ron and I could hear her moan every time they poked her to try and find a vein. She was too weak to cry out loud. It made us feel so helpless and we could hardly stand it. I remember the doctor talking to us in the hallway, just outside the emergency room where there was a crew of doctors and nurses trying to find a vein in Cheryl. He stated his amazement that Ron and I were both carriers of Cystinosis. After all, he had looked after our two nephews and knew how rare the disease was. He suggested we go home to our family and get some sleep and be with our other daughter, Lori, who was only three at the time. She needed us at home because she was too young to understand why we were away so long. He assured us that if anything should go wrong they would call us. We had confidence in the hospital staff. There was nothing we could do there.

Once again we asked God to give us the strength and courage we needed to cope with this.

The next morning I was so happy and relieved to see Cheryl awake and doing much better. She had tubes coming from her head and hand and I thanked God that she was doing as well as she was. I remember counting the needle pokes that she had received in order for them to find a vein and when I reached 17 pokes I quit because it bothered me too much to think of the pain she had to go through for the intravenous. Cheryl remained in the hospital for twelve days. Before being released and because of her problem of failure to thrive, secondary to malnutrition, Cheryl was started on nasogastric tube feeding with Ensure. I was instructed on the technique for nasogastric tube feeding, and Cheryl steadily regained her weight. She came home on her dad's birthday, March 15, 1985.

Again, there were rough and difficult times. I tube fed Cheryl all of her foods for about a year, including her medication and of course whipping cream, to try and fatten her up and get her strength back. This tube was inserted in her nose and down to her stomach three times a day. After tube feeding her for a year, she started eating on her own and we encountered no problems. We had comments from people that tube feeding wasn't good because she wouldn't learn how to eat. This simply wasn't true. Cheryl gained strength and began to walk by 21 months. I continued tube feeding her medication and whipping cream for another six months.

Cheryl became a patient of a genetics specialist, who had met a doctor from San Diego at a Vancouver conference. They discussed Cheryl and he asked if Cheryl would participate in a new drug study. All that was requested was our permission and that of the Board of Ethics Committee in Canada in November of 1985. The Californian doctor explained that there would be no side effects and hopefully the damage to the kidney would be arrested. A transplant could be as distant as 30 years.

Cheryl received her new drug on January 13, 1985. We said that it was her miracle drug because she received it on the anniversary date that

her older cousin had died. We said that he was her guardian angel and he was looking after her.

She immediately responded to the new drug without vomiting and could only take it with milk as a chaser. The only time she did vomit was when we tried to increase her dosage too quickly.

Up to the age of four, we rushed Cheryl to the hospital several times. We noticed something wrong when her thumbs turned in and her fingers started to cripple. Her calcium was low. At the hospital, she was treated intravenously with calcium supplement. Other times we rushed Cheryl in because her potassium was too low. These symptoms were different. She would wake up in the night too weak to hold herself up. Hospital staff brought her level back up with Pedialyte. Later I was asked if I would give it to her myself. After that, when we noticed her getting low at home we would give her the Pedialyte ourselves. She would quickly bounce back. It was this time that we stopped NG feeding all together.

I remember the last rushed overnight visit in the hospital. It was a Friday in June 1987 and I was packing to go the lake. All day long I was hesitant as I watched Cheryl lay on her blanket in the middle of the kitchen floor. She wasn't saying or doing anything and looked sick. I told myself that I could take care of her just as well at the lake as at home. Perhaps the sun and the beach would brighten her up. Unfortunately, as I watched her, diarrhea poured out and we had to rush her to the hospital. She had the flu and was quite dehydrated.

Ron was unloading the trunk at home when the phone rang. It was my mother calling him to take her to the hospital right away. It was her heart.

Again, another difficult time. Ron and my mother were in one hospital while I was in another with Cheryl. That's life. However, my mother is doing quite well now.

Cheryl started nursery school in September 1987 and was never rushed to the hospital again. She became strong and remained so with all of her medications and care she received at home.

Cheryl went to the hospital for check-ups every three months and was monitored, expertly by her genetics specialist and two pediatric nephrologists.

On June 8, 1993, Cheryl started on growth hormone and grew over four inches in one year. That meant giving her a needle every day until her transplant. Then on June 7, 1994 she was given a blood transfusion because she was anemic. The normal blood level for a child her age is between 117 and 150 and Cheryl's blood level was only 70. After the transfusion, her level was 107. To avoid anemia we would give her a weekly needle, but as we got closer to the transplant date, her blood level was monitored and her weekly needle had to be increases to two needles in a week, then three a week. She looked really healthy, but thin, with a pale complexion and she often had dark circles under her eyes. She tired quickly but had a very good appetite and craved and enjoyed many different foods. The doctor told us to keep her healthy by giving her anything she craved so that the calorie intake was high. That meant a lot of McDonald's burgers. I remember how at bedtime she would ask for a snack of "Gourmet food." That meant Eggs Benedict, which is still her favorite dish today.

When Cheryl was eleven her transplant date was set for October 1995. Visits with the pediatric nephrologists became more frequent and as the date grew closer the visits increased to every week. The last visit indicated that the transplant date had to be moved up to September.

Ron and I were both tested because we wanted to give her a kidney, thereby increasing her chances against rejection. We were both matches and decided separately that Ron would be the better candidate. I was more capable of caring for Ron and Cheryl after the transplant. I was fortunate to work at my children's school and they were extremely supportive and sympathetic about taking time off. Ron's decision was precious. He said that I had given birth to our four children and it was his turn to do something for one of our children. Also, Ron would receive full coverage at his workplace. God does look after us.

Cheryl received a kidney transplant on September 28, 1995 and Ron was the donor. Ron recovered quickly and was back home in three days and Cheryl had a miraculous recovery. She returned home in five days and did very well for six months. In her sixth month she had a rejection bout which was brought under control very quickly. Exactly a year later Cheryl had another rejection bout, and the nephrologist changed medications. Cheryl has been doing extremely well since and continues to go for a monthly checkup to determine medication amounts.

Fortunately for us today, the worst is over. Cheryl is doing so well that most of her school friends suspect nothing of her situation. All of her medications are pill form and quite easy to take, even though she takes 38 pills a day.

She surpassed our goal of five feet in height by more than an inch, and weighs 104 lbs. She is a full time student in grade twelve, graduating in June, and working part time at a fast food restaurant. She loves to party and socialize.

We count this as a blessing as it allows us to now spend more time with our grown children and grandchildren. Cheryl is able to care for her own needs and is becoming very independent.

Christine being 17 years older, never spent very much time with Cheryl because she was busy attending high school at the time, then went to University and worked part time as well. She became a mother to Michael and Lori in our absence. Christine had to learn how to face the fact that her sister was born with a disease that had taken the lives of her two very close cousins. How could this happen? She had a difficult time to accept and deal with it. She owes her deep faith by witnessing her parents' acceptance of the situation. Her faith in God was molded in those critical years.

Michael was seven years old when Cheryl was born. We are thankful now for the time we shared with him before Cheryl came along. He had a lovable nature, was very affectionate, and a well-adjusted brother. He accepted the situation well because Christine was there to look after him (one of his three parents). Michael was very easy to please, and being a very neat child, made looking after him quite easy. He was always joking, smiling and happy. Today Michael takes the responsibility of asking Cheryl if she has taken her medications, supervises her parties, and talks to her about certain curfews she breaks.

Lori was the one that had to sacrifice a lot. She was only two and a half when Cheryl started getting sick. Her stubborn temperament was already showing. Lori was always patient, kind and generous when it came to spending time with Cheryl. She was never jealous of Cheryl, but played with her, shared her toys and always made sure that Cheryl was happy. When Lori started school we worried about her stubborn nature, but to our amazement, she was a perfect student. She took her frustrations and anger out on us as a family. It took us a while to realize her behavior towards us and understand. Lori was not as affectionate towards me because I spent more time with Cheryl. Only now, in her later teen years is she able to give me a hug. I always showed her affection. I held her in my arms and gave her hugs, but she seemed to push me away. Sometimes it hurt, but I knew why. I knew her rejection wouldn't last forever. Today when she goes away on one of her outdoor excursions, she will hug me good-bye. It warms my heart.

Ron and I have always loved our children very much and tried to teach them to accept things as they are and ask God to help us to accept and give us the strength to be able to survive any obstacles that come our way.

Living with a member of the family that has a kidney disease has now become an easy task. The daily reminder of, "Did you take your medications?" will always be there, and making sure that prescriptions are up to date.

The nature and character of our children were not affected very much by Cheryl's illness, but no doubt everyone had to make great sacrifices.

KIDNEYS

URETERS

BLADDER

URETHRA

Eryk Spiry is a 3-year-old boy with Prune Belly Syndrome.

Hi, my name is Eryk and I have Prune Belly Syndrome. I just turned three on July 17th, 2001. My mommy wants to share with everyone why I am her "biggest" Little Hero...

Mommy said that she and Daddy found out I had urinary and kidney problems when she was just 21 weeks pregnant with me. What started out as a routine ultrasound turned out to be a little more serious.

Mommy and Daddy were really scared when they had to go see the fetal assessment team! The first appointment made Mom and Dad really upset because they found out my bladder, kidneys, and ureters were really dilated. The doctors said that I probably had a tiny blockage somewhere in my urinary tract that prevented the urine from draining out. They also said that there wasn't much that could be done and that they would keep monitoring me every week and hopefully I would make it to full term. My Mom and Dad spent the next three weeks really worrying as they waited for the amnio results to come back...and they came back normal!

My mommy was induced five weeks early. The doctors needed to get me out so they could drain all the urine out of me. I had to stay

> What started out as a routine ultrasound turned out to be a little more serious.

Eryk

in the NICU for one and a half months while the doctors tried to get my urinary tract figured out (I think I had them a little confused at first!), but they did it and I came home in September.

Having Prune Belly Syndrome means that I was born with mega-ureters, dilated kidneys, undescended testes, a huge bladder, limited kidney function with re-flux on the right side, and no abdominal muscles. I had a six hour operation when I was nine months old to correct some of the damage and give me more support with my tummy muscles.

Now, I have a little kidney function on the left side and my right kidney is damaged but doing its part for now. I have to take different yucky tasting medicines every day. The doctors aren't sure when I will need dialysis or a transplant, but as far as we know, it's not in the near future (thank goodness!).

My mom and dad want to say "thank-you" to NICU, urology and nephrology for figuring out what was going on and fixing up my urinary tract…to my pediatrician, because he makes my mommy feel better with her endless questions!…to my physical therapist, my occupational therapist, and my special needs daycare worker, for helping me get up and walking and learning so much!…and to Grandma, for helping my mommy and daddy out whenever I am in the hospital (luv-yu!).

Sincerely,
Eryk

Gerlyn

Gerlyn Strachan is a 15-year-old girl who had one failed transplant and received her second transplant from her mother in 2002. She was diagnosed with dysfibrinogemia at the age of 8.

Hello, My name is Gerlyn Pearl Strachan and I am 15 years old. At the age of eight I was diagnosed with dysfibrinogenemia, which is a fibrinogen disorder in the blood. I was a normal eight year old, active and always smiling until I started to have back pain and feeling sick.

My mom took me to our family doctor and he said that all I had was stomach flu. We went home, with the awful tasting liquid antibiotic that I hated, thinking that everything was okay and I would feel better in a couple of days. Two days passed and I was not feeling any better, but getting worse. So my parents decided to take me to the Children's Hospital Emergency. The doctor at the emergency told my parents the same thing that our family doctor told my mom. He gave me another type of antibiotic and told my parents that I to go back to the emergency if I got dehydrated within 6 to 8 hours. I was not dehydrated but getting worse everyday so four days later my mom took me to my pediatrician. He was very helpful and sent me to the Children's Clinic for blood work.

At around 7:30 pm that night my pediatrician phoned my parents to bring me to the Children's Hospital to be admitted and take more tests because they found something wrong in my blood from the tests that they took earlier that day. By the time we got to the hospital it was around 9:00 pm. They did some blood tests and this was done urgently. As you know when you walk into the emergency you have to wait forever. They also called me to go for an ultrasound. It didn't take very long to get the results. Doctors came to see us in the waiting room to take us to a private room. The doctors told my parents that they were very sorry to inform us that both of my kidneys had collapsed. I didn't really understand what was going on. I thought that I was just going to get some medicine and then I would be all right, but that was just one of the things that they did. By the time all of this had happened it was already 2:30 in the morning of March 22,1996.

After the doctors came to talk to us I was admitted to the intensive care unit to keep a close eye on me. That morning I had my first surgery to put a peritoneal dialysis catheter in, I was scared going in for my first surgery, but my family was by my side all the time. I stayed on peritoneal dialysis for 8 months until my kidneys started to function just enough for me to be able to come off dialysis. For 3 years I was off of dialysis. When my creatinine started to go up, the doctors decided to put me back on dialysis because they wanted me to stay healthy and strong for when a kidney became available. I had my peritoneal catheter put back in on October 4,1999 and I was on peritoneal dialysis for 10 hours a day for 6 nights a week.

On January 16, 2000 at around 9:00am my mom got a call from the doctor to bring me into the hospital because a cadaveric donor transplant was available for me. I cried because I was scared and very nervous but my family were and always have been very supportive. I

> I didn't really understand what was going on. I thought that I was just going to get some medicine and then I would be all right...

had the transplant late that night. Unfortunately the new kidney had rejected my body because a vein to the kidney had a clot. Three days after I had the kidney transplant I had to go for another surgery to remove the transplanted kidney. I recovered fully from this surgery and went back to my normal activities. I didn't let any of this interfere with my activities and school. I am very dedicated to school. The things I like to do at school are work hard and get good grades and see my friends. My friends have been very understanding with all of this stuff happening to me.

After the cadaveric donor transplant didn't work out I stayed on dialysis until October 1st, 2002. You must be thinking, why only until Oct.1/02? Well, that is because I had another match for a new kidney. This time it was a living donor transplant, and the person who was giving me a new kidney was my mom. This transplant took place on Oct.3/02. Before this date my mom had to go for lots of tests to make sure that her kidneys were working fine and were healthy. My mom and I were very excited, as were my dad and brother. A couple days before the transplant I was admitted to get a central line put in. There were complications so I had to go for another surgery to get the central line fixed, so it would work better. It finally worked out. Two days later it was the day of the transplant. The worst part of the day for me was waiting until it was my time to go in the Operating Room. Finally, the time had come and I started to feel a little bit

Gerlyn

nervous, but I knew that everything would work out good. The surgery for my mom lasted for about 3 to 4 hours and mine was for 2 to 3 hours. After the surgery I was put into the Intensive Care Unit. Everyone in my family were on their toes for the first week, because in the first transplant the rejection happened in the first 3 days. When that first week passed, everyone felt better and more calm. By the time I was up and moving they moved me to the ward of the Children's Hospital. Everything was working out great and my new kidney had a slow start but got going after.

My dad and I had some teaching on how to take my new medications properly. At first it was a lot but the doctors at times decreased some doses depending on my blood results. About a week after the transplant I went home. When we went home, we still had to get up early in the morning to go to the transplant clinic. This went on for about a month and then they started to see me twice a week. Currently they are seeing me once a week. A month later I had my first biopsy and had my peritoneal dialysis catheter and central line taken out. Everything went well and here I am 2 months later feeling fine and happy that everything worked out.

After the transplant I could really see a difference in the way that I felt. I could now eat breakfast in the morning; before the transplant I wasn't eating breakfast because I didn't have the appetite. I could also see that I wasn't tired like I was before. Before I used to get tired easily. There was also a change in my face, my face was now more round around the cheek areas but that was a side affect from one of the medications that I was taking. I am very happy with the end result.

Since I was diagnosed in 1996, I received very good treatment from the whole nephrology team. I am very grateful, together with my mom, dad, and brother for such a dedicated team at the Children's Hospital who do all the research and everything else that they have done for me to improve my health to what it is today. My sincere thanks to all of them.

Gerlyn

Amber

Ron and Jean Taraschuck are the parents of Amber, a 16-year-old girl with ARPKD and whose treatments have included dialysis and a transplant.

Finally we were at home, isolated and scared to make mistakes.

Amber was diagnosed with polycystic kidneys when she was ten months old. One day she would require dialysis and eventually a transplant. This news just floored my wife and I. I guess the shock never really goes away, but is tucked away only to re-awaken.

Well, life went on. Amber went for more check ups and was given particular medications, restrictions from contact sports, and apparently, was spoiled by Dad (so I'm told to this day).

You know, over time things pass until one day, the realization hits you. Amber's condition had deteriorated to the point where dialysis was required. She was twelve and a half years old. Boy, time flies.

God only knows what went through Amber's mind, never mind what went through our own. We ensured that Amber was at each and every meeting with various doctors throughout this crisis, as well as ensuring she had as normal a childhood as possible within her restrictions.

Dialysis training came and went. Gastrosomy tube feeding training came and went. EPO injections came (uncomfortably) and went, and then the big day. Finally we were at home, isolated and scared to make mistakes. This was our first night to "connect" Amber alone. Following our training and trouble shooting guides, we managed.

Throughout all of this came a lot of uncertainties along with the patience of the doctors and pediatric nephrology support staff. Even still it sure takes a toll on family life. There was so little time for ourselves as parents. I guess it depends on each individual case, but as parents, and with the love for your child, you persevere quietly.

Life was sure hectic, especially for Amber who had numerous other problems semi-related to her kidney disease.

Twenty-two months later, we received a call from her doctor. A kidney was possibly available. We'll never forget Sunday, January 16, 2000, 10:30 am. Momentarily, I was brain dead. Nothing registered. This was so unexpected and unbelievable. Anxiety rose several levels that day as Amber prepared for surgery.

Initially we met with success. The kidney took and monitoring, tests, check ups, following up on anything out of the ordinary were constant. Amber's taking of medication had to be watched closely and religiously to ensure success. Words still can not express how we all felt. A great burden had been released, but with new direction and concerns.

Well, as life would have it, fifteen months later, due to complications, we were told Amber's kidney was showing signs of rejection. What can you say? Hemo-dialysis was the only recourse.

So, life goes on. A new set of problems, worries and concerns, not for ourselves, but for Amber. A fifteen year old doesn't need or deserve this, but what can you do?

Another day will come and the phone will ring. Life will turn another page and hopefully deliver a very happy ending.

Thank you to those who have helped us and especially Amber over the years. Your support, kind and (deserved) strict words, have been appreciated.

Amber, my wife, and I would also like to take this opportunity to thank someone very, very special. Unknowingly, you gave our daughter a chance to live, enjoy life (as a teenager should) and not be sustained by machines. There is not a moment when I talk, laugh or scold Amber that I don't think of you and your family. Perhaps the only words of comfort we can offer are that, when we look into Amber's eyes, we also feel your loved one.

Thank you. Thank you for another chance.

Kyle

Janet and Gord Turner are the parents of Kyle, a 14-year-old boy who received a kidney transplant from his father in 1999.

While every child is special and a hero in some ways, these young men and women have to endure more than the average child. For everything they go through, they truly are Little Heroes...

The Beginning:

On September 23 1999, just 12 days before my son's 11th birthday, he had a kidney transplant. It was something that we knew was a possibility from the time he was 18 months old...

Kyle started walking just around his first birthday and by 16 months his little bowed legs seemed to be getting worse instead of better. So after a couple of trips to our pediatrician, it was recommended that Kyle see a bone specialist. After some x-rays and blood tests, the bone specialist and pediatrician concluded that Kyle had rickets.

"How can a boy that has yogurt for breakfast, cheese sandwiches for lunch and as much milk as we can give him, have rickets!" I wondered out loud to the doctors.

An ultrasound revealed the unbelievable answer: Kyle was born with only one kidney and it was only 25% formed and 10%

functioning! His little kidney was filtering out calcium thinking it was a waste product, instead of sending it to his bones! At the time of his diagnosis, it seemed a transplant was in the very near future, but after being put on medication to help the kidney and vitamin D to strengthen Kyle's bones, the diagnosis changed. It seemed as if that little kidney was more determined to be useful than even the doctors realized and a transplant was put on hold.

Knowing the Medical System:

As a parent, being associated with a teaching hospital has its positive and negative aspects in the form of resident doctors. The resident doctor will come in before your regular doctor and ask you questions about your child that you feel you have answered a dozen times before. It is hard to be patient and smile while you are wondering why they just don't read the 5-inch thick chart in their hand, but the reality is you are the testing ground for these soon-to-be nephrologists. Use them to your advantage by asking questions. The truth is these residents are still reading text books, attending lectures and making sure that they know the kidney inside and out well enough to pass exams. They are a fountain of knowledge. Sometimes they may surprise you, like the time a resident thought he heard a "rattle" in Kyle's chest, had the nephrolgist listen, and it was the beginning of a chest infection. Since Kyle hadn't even developed any symptoms yet the resident saved us at least one sleepless night with a sick kid and a trip to the pediatrician.

It is hard to be patient and smile while you are wondering why they just don't read the 5-inch thick chart in their hand...

Growth Hormone:

Kyle progressed very well over the next few years and the only concern seemed to be his height or lack of it! As with most kids with kidney problems, the natural growth hormone is seen as a waste product by the kidney and filtered out of the body. This was keeping Kyle well below the 5th percentile for height in his age group. Then, when Kyle was 4, the nephrology doctors approached us about a new study. A European company was sponsoring kidney patients who fell into a certain criteria to take artificial growth hormone to see if it would help their stature as it had with kids with pituitary gland problems. The study was originally set for 2 years with the possibility of a longer trial if the results were what the company hoped for. The catch was the only way to administer the hormone was through daily injections given to Kyle by my husband Gord and me. We thought it over and read all of the information made available to us from the doctors, nurses and the drug company. It seemed the growth hormone would not only stimulate his growth but also his failing appetite. These two things together would make him not only taller but also more importantly healthier.

Kyle was very brave and the results were amazing! Little by little his height crept up the chart and soon he was only a small amount shorter than friends his age. By the time he reached grade one he was no longer the smallest in the class.

Kyle was and is the poster child for why kidney patients should take growth hormone. His appetite was normal, his energy level was normal, he wasn't the shortest kid in the class, and besides taking medication daily and monthly doctor appointments, he was just like any other kid his age. He played soccer, baseball, basketball, and was not missing as much school due to illness. We were glad to hear the kidney doctor joke with Kyle that he was totally boring. When the study for the growth hormone ended 6 years later, the doctors informed us that it was now available with a prescription and covered by Pharmacare. Although it is a very expensive medication, and we quickly reached our deductible each year, we gladly paid our share to keep Kyle taking the injections.

Dad as a Donor:

As the doctors became accustomed to how to regulate Kyle's medications with each new growth spurt, it was becoming apparent to them that the medications he was on would be able to keep him stable only until the onset of puberty. As we all remember, hormones wildly fluctuate at this time and this would cause, in Kyle, drug levels to be out of whack. It started to happen when Kyle was in Grade 4. He was 10-1/2 and getting tired while playing soccer and basketball. His creatinine levels were getting higher and higher with each appointment and the doctors approached us about being tested as possible donors for a living related transplant. It was everyone's hope that the transplant could take place before the kidney failed, in order to avoid dialysis. I was ruled out in the first round of tests. My blood type was not compatible. My husband Gord says he always knew he would be the donor. I kept telling him not to be too optimistic so that if he were unable to donate he would be better able to handle the news. He would just smile and say, "I am going to be the donor and you are going to take good care of us when we get home from the hospital." Gord was right. He was a terrific match. He would be the donor.

It was now May 1999, and at each appointment the doctors and nurses began to prepare us for the transplant. We were all encouraged to write down any questions and pre-transplant appointments were made with the surgeons and the transplant co-coordinator. The co-ordinator met with us quite a few times before the surgery and by the time the date was set, we felt very prepared. The date was set; September 23rd 1999 would be the big day! Gord joked that this would make Kyle Y2K ready.

Transplant Day:

The day before the transplant Gord and Kyle checked into the Children's Hospital in Winnipeg. Kyle and Gord were in the same room. I think it was really great that they let Gord stay in Children's Hospital instead of going to the Adult General Hospital. It was very beneficial for both of them to be together the night before the transplant. In the morning they came and got Gord first. I was able to go with him to the OR, but I would not see him right after the kidney was removed. He would be groggy and on medication so the nurses and doctors felt it would be better if we saw each other when he was back in his room. The nurses assured us they would update Gord on Kyle's progress. When Gord was done his surgery he was asked to rate the pain on a scale of 1 to 10; 10 being the worst pain you've ever felt in your life. He remembers starting with 6 and quickly moving up from there. His advice to other transplant donors: "It is 10! No need to be brave now, just say 10!"

Just before it was time for Kyle to go into surgery, the nurses came to let us know Gord was doing very well and they had no problem removing the kidney. "I think that kidney is looking for a new home Kyle," our nurse smiled as she went to get a wheelchair for Kyle.

Kyle was very brave when it was time for his surgery. He was surprisingly calm until about 10 minutes before he was scheduled to go in. Luckily his surgeon was also a magician! He did a few magic tricks right there in the hallway and made Kyle smile. I took a deep breath, smiled and waved as they wheeled him into his surgery.

A few hours later the doctors found me in the lounge by the OR. As they approached, smiling and joking, I knew all went well. They informed me that Kyle was waking up in the recovery room and would love to see his Mom. He looked a little tired, but the pain was well under control and he told me about how they put him to sleep and how funny he thought the surgeon was. Before the transplant we were told he could be in recovery for quite a few hours and then he would be moved to Children's ICU for the night. He ended up doing so well that he was only in recovery for a few hours and then he was moved back up to Children's Hospital ward for the night!

Gord was understandably very tired and they were both hooked up to IV and blood pressure machines that were going to beep all night. The nurses thought it best for the first few days, that Gord and Kyle not be in the same room. Kyle watched an episode of Friends on TV that same night and then moved on to Nintendo. When it was time for Kyle to go to sleep,

Kyle

the nurses advised me to go home and get some rest. They assured me Kyle would sleep through the night, but with all the beeping I would not. It was hard to leave, but I knew they were both in great hands.

After a couple of days, they were able to be in the same room. I think that really helped their recovery time. They were able to see that the other was recovering nicely. Soon, the doctors reminded Gord that it was time to get out of bed and start walking around. He said he got a few confused looks from parents and kids as he walked the halls of the fifth floor of the Children's Hospital in his hospital gown! The next few days went by quickly as both Gord and Kyle began their recovery from surgery. Kyle was feeling healthier and more energetic as each day passed and luckily neither of them had any complications after surgery. They both agree that the worst part of the whole process can be summed up with one word:
Catheter!!

Gord was in the hospital for only 5 days and Kyle got out a day later. We had prepared Kyle for spending his 11th birthday in the hospital, but he was at home with his parents, brother and Grandma. In the weeks following the transplant, Kyle had a tutor come to our house and help him with his schoolwork. He missed his friends, but he was allowed to have healthy visitors at home. He was allowed to go out with his brother for Halloween and to go to his classroom on a couple of occasions to participate in some art activities. He was not scheduled to go back to the classroom until after the Christmas break, but again he shocked us with being so healthy that he was back in class just 6 weeks after the transplant!

Normal Life:

It has been 3 years since Gord donated his kidney to Kyle and both are still very healthy. When Kyle is asked about the negative aspects of having a kidney transplant he has a hard time thinking of one. He did say however, that he doesn't like wearing the protective pad over the transplanted kidney required during sports. Now if that is the only negative thing a 14 year old can come up with then I'd say that's pretty great!

The purpose of the kidney transplant, besides the obvious health benefits, is to help the recipient lead a normal life. Kyle is a normal teenager! He forgets to do his homework, he loves computer games, his room is a mess, he likes watching The Simpson's, he doesn't want us to know he likes girls, he has his own ideas about what to wear, how to dress, and is embarrassed by his parents. But more importantly, he plays on the basketball team, the volleyball team, loves to play street hockey with his brother, his height is normal, he feels good and his self esteem is very high. Even when it comes to taking his pills, he does not feel differently from the kids his age. He knows other kids have to take medication for things like diabetes and asthma and he is very responsible when it comes to taking his medication. He knows what a precious gift he has received from his Dad and he does not want to lose it.

Justin Says:

Justin is Kyle's younger bother by 4 years. He is very understanding and mature about Kyle's experiences and will even remind him to take his pills. Justin thinks his aunts and uncles and grandparents treat Kyle the same, but when we see friends or relatives that have not seen Kyle for a long time they tend to focus their attention and questions on him. Justin says the only thing that really bothers him about Kyle's kidney problems is after biopsies. Strenuous activity is not allowed for two weeks so this means Justin does not have a goalie for street hockey. Justin also mentioned that he doesn't think it is fair that Kyle gets all of the attention for being so brave during the transplant, when he feels his Dad was just as brave, if not braver. Sometimes Justin feels that his Dad should get more recognition.

Attitude is Everything:

With all that we've been through as a family, I still maintain that we are truly blessed. Looking back to the time when Kyle was first diagnosed with kidney problems, it was, of course a shock. We went through a sad and confusing time, but we soon realized that there was nothing we could do to change the

Kidney disease is part of your life; it is not your whole life.

Kyle

circumstances; we just had to find a way to deal with them.

Things could have been so much more difficult and tragic, and the fact is every thing that could go right did. Maintaining a positive attitude does amazing things for yourself, your family and especially for your child with kidney disease. Of course you are human and stress and anger are normal, but it is important to keep it in perspective and under control. Kidney disease is part of your life; it is not your whole life. The most important advise we can give to other parents and their families is to be as positive as you can and ask questions.

Gord summed up our experience best: There were speed bumps on the road we traveled, but many individuals along the way have supported us, and it's a path that has been well worthwhile.

Janet, Gord, Kyle and Justin Turner…

Ashley-Marie

Shelley-Marie Olivier and Allan Young are the parents of Ashley-Marie, a 5-year-old girl with William's Syndrome whose treatment has included peritoneal dialysis. Ashley-Marie had a kidney transplant in 2004.

Our daughter Ashley-Marie was born nine weeks early on February 4, 1998. She weighed only 3lbs 13ozs at birth. She was born on a Wednesday and by Friday the doctors had already discovered that she had abnormalities. They discussed with us the possibility that she wouldn't survive all her problems and believed she had "William's Syndrome". They couldn't confirm this yet and asked about doing tests to confirm their belief.

When they told us, we were devastated because we took all the precautions and advice of our doctor. During the pregnancy we were aware of partial placenta previa. We couldn't understand why this was happening to her and us. She also has a 10 year-old brother Devin and a 2-year-old sister Amber-Marie.

We had a lot of doctor's appointments. With so many doctors and specialists, keeping track of them is a full time job in itself. This seemed to lighten up a little once everyone had their tests done and all had agreed on Ashley-Marie's diagnosis.

There is so much to tell you about this sweet little girl. She had so many other problems along with kidney disease but it all works around the various illnesses that comes with "William's Syndrome". There is so much emotional turmoil with this type of beginning to your child's early life. She had to go to the doctor for everything. Even for things that you would normally wait out or give your child medicine to help. With Ashley-Marie, even fevers could turn real bad very quickly. So we were always on edge around anyone who was sick or had colds or even just going to the store. She wasn't allowed to come out for the first 2 years of her life. She was always having blood tests to make sure all her levels were all right and we had to just tolerate her always crying.

We were seeing the kidney doctor every 3 months at first. Always hoping that everything was going to be OK with her results. She had been on sodium from birth and we always had to get it into her somehow. For the first 2 years we spent most of our time going back and forth to the doctors and specialists. We really didn't have much time to understand and process the disease. It was only after the second year that we really started to look at the disease and process the oncoming challenges that our "little fighter" had yet to go through.

It was so hard to watch her go through all the pain and suffering with all the testing. We were getting information from the doctors regarding the challenges she would yet need to face. It was upsetting knowing what we had to go through. It was only going to get harder on her. We've had a lot of ups and downs with her kidney disease. With all the advice from the specialists we did have some comfort that we had all these great doctors to look after our precious daughter because we had no idea what to do. We were told that her kidneys were growing along with her right now and they would postpone medications or surgery until there was concern that her kidneys were not functioning properly for her body needs.

When we look at all the pain and suffering she has gone through, we realize how strong she is. We needed to be as strong as she. All the doctors became like an extended family. They got to know us just as much as your family does. You seem to talk to them just as much as your family. They need to know everything about you and your spouse's family, so they can keep up on any possible problems to come.

For the first 2 years we just had to monitor the kidney and wait and see what comes in the future. There has been so much more for her to overcome. We have had to look at the big picture and not concentrate on a specific thing because there are so many things to have to watch over.

Now Ashley-Marie is 5 years old and there has been so many things changing in her life. I'm going to talk about all her experiences and ours as a family.

Ashley-Marie started to lose weight and her kidneys were beginning to fail even further. We were approached by the Renal Dietician about surgically placing a gastrostomy (feeding) tube into her stomach. We were suddenly hit with a tremendous amount of fear. Up until now, it had been a lot of talk and a wait and see game. Now we were at the point of surgeries and a lot of questions and medical interventions. Ashley-Marie stopped eating and was getting worse so our choice was to implant the feeding (G-Tube) on her 2nd birthday – Feb 4/02. Surgery went well and we began the training in the hospital on how to use the machine and feed our daughter all over again. She had a lot of problems healing after the surgery but we started her feeding regimen.

She was doing very well within a couple of weeks. She gained 5 lbs and was doing better all around. Her kidneys had stabilized again. Of course through all this she was still a happy- go–lucky kind of child. It was unbelievable that she could still be so happy with all the things around her changing so much. Suddenly she started to have problems with throwing up and she started to lose weight. Her kidneys were beginning to have more problems. We slowly started to feed her again in smaller amounts and watched to see what she could handle without throwing up.

During this time there's a lot of trial and error on the parents' part. I found this to be very hard and stressful. You need to learn what is best for

Ashley-Marie

her. We're only parents and not medically trained to deal with these kinds of situations. Things change so fast, we as parents don't have time to take in these facts. It's like all of a sudden becoming nurses & doctors in a sense. You have to notice any little changes and determine what should be your next step. Finally this was under control.

We had a very bad experience with the G-Tube. We had company over and we started Ashley-Marie on her normal tube feeding that evening. Suddenly, she screamed and we turned around to see her feeding tube had been pulled out of her stomach. Unbelievable thoughts went through our heads. We packed Ashley-Marie up and rushed off to the hospital. They asked me if I had brought the new tubing with us. I felt very emotionally distraught. I felt no one understood how we were feeling in this situation. This was our first bad experience and being a parent we don't normally remember the medical aspects first. The experience is very stressful. This is a very scary and vulnerable time for parents. Our children are everything and you start to question your abilities as a parent.

Medical staff must understand that we are still only parents and not trained medically. We've had a lot of things to remember and learn. It's hard for an everyday parent to be able to deal with all these kinds of things. It takes a lot to be a parent with a child that is sick. There are so many unanswered questions and so much information that you need to know. You feel very overwhelmed very often and tend to look to see what you've done wrong.

She's now doing well and we've adjusted. We've now been told her kidney is failing and they have to look at doing the surgery to insert a peritoneal dialysis catheter. They are planning a surgery date and we are discussing how aggressive we want to be. We decided it is in her best interest to go ahead with the dialysis. The surgery date was planned for February 4, 2002, just two weeks after the discussions started. We weren't really ready for it.

We are trying to be very comforting to our daughter but at the same time we're having our own problems dealing with the procedure and what's to follow. When they did the surgery for the dialysis catheter, they also did a heart ECG (electrocardiogram). I was in the recovery room and I saw the heart doctors come in. My heart started to beat extremely fast and I was worried. Your child goes in without worries and comes out with larger problems that had not been expected or noticed. They talked about needing surgery for her heart as soon as possible. Their findings were just unbelievable. She did have heart problems but this was not even thought of. They had discussed their findings and we met the next day to talk about the next step. They wanted to do a test to back up the information 100% and we went along with that idea. This was such an extreme problem and there was concern that they wouldn't be able to fix it. We felt overwhelmed with the possibility of heart surgery in 2 weeks. We just didn't know if we could get through this. Then they found that she fell into that one percent of patients who show incorrect readings and was not affected to the extent that they had thought.

Now she has had the dialysis surgery and is doing OK. We travelled for the next 8 weeks to the hospital once per week for sterile dressing changes to her PD catheter. She was healing so much better than expected since the last G-Tube surgeries. We waited to see when the dialysis would start. We did blood tests every month to see how the kidneys were functioning and when she should start dialysis. We trained to learn how to do the dialysis at home. It was intense for one week every afternoon learning what would be required to carry out this procedure at home each night. Questions of when we or family members could be tested for the kidney transplant had always been on our mind but now became a reality.

While all these things were happening, we were also in the middle of getting recommendations from doctors and other programs to build a badly needed addition to our home. We house 7 people in a small 1 and a half story house. We have been very lucky because my mother has been able to care for our children in the daytime when we're both working. When Ashley-Marie first started on all the medications for her kidneys, we had to pay for it. This took two incomes and with all the traveling back and forth to the doctors (one whole 8 hr day just for these appointments), things were very stressful financially. There were so many helpful people in the organizations. It's just unbelievable the number of people willing to lend a hand with things. There has been a social evening to help with the costly care and house addition. We received a lot of support from family, friends, co-workers, organizations and businesses.

Next we ran into a problem with her dialysis catheter coming out of her abdomen and she had an infection in her surgical area. They needed to remove the catheter and place it on the other side of her abdomen and treat the infection. We were lucky that she wasn't actually using it for dialysis yet. This way we could treat and correct things without too many other problems.

With all this stuff happening around us we don't have time to get down. We've had all of our concentration on correcting things and taking care of these problems. You don't really get time to sit and think about all the pain and suffering your young child has been going through.

🐝 *Ashley-Marie*

Ashley-Marie is only 17 lbs. and very short in length. There were discussions about her not being the appropriate size for a transplant. They referred us to Pediatric Endocrinology to see if she would be a candidate for growth hormone injections. We've started these injections and for the last couple of months she's growing. This is due to the injections and dialysis. There are of course side effects with the injections that just terrify us, but we need to do what is necessary to help her grow and prepare her for the upcoming transplant. Giving needles to our little girl does take a lot of strength that sometimes we just haven't got.

It is now December 2002 and Ashley-Marie has been on dialysis and the growth hormone since October 2002. We've had a lot of roadblocks along the way. She has been doing remarkably well for all she has gone through. She has reached a lot of milestones lately and is trying to stand and makes the effort to walk. Her vocabulary is so much better. We had always wondered if she would be able to do everything that a healthy child does and, as always, she just astonishes us with her will and fight for life. She doesn't have normal nights as she must be hooked up to her dialysis by 6:30 pm. As she is in bed by that time, it makes it impossible for her to move around and enjoy play time with the other children. We are making plans for her to go to school next year with the aid of a wheelchair. She hasn't got the strength to stand for any period of time other than for about 30 seconds.

We've had time now to focus more on her dialysis and the prognosis. When you see a loved one, especially children, fighting for such things as our daughter, it makes you more appreciative of all of the things healthy people

> She has taught me and others around me more about ourselves and how to just enjoy the moment and not worry about tomorrow.

take for granted. If it wasn't for her loving and accepting ways, there is no way we as a family could help her get through all these medical obstacles. As the mom of this little sweetheart, I feel overwhelmed most of the time. I always feel better when I think of all the things my daughter has overcome. She always puts in 100% effort. She does make me think a lot clearer about everything I do in my life. I'm always scared of what tomorrow will bring but just seeing her laughing and fighting with her sister and brother makes things better. She has taught me and others around me more about ourselves and how to just enjoy the moment and not worry about tomorrow.

Thanks again to everyone that has lent a helping hand and support through these trying times.

Just a Mom!

Note: Ashley-Marie received a kidney from her father in 2004.

Ashley-Marie

Sherry and Glen Weaver are the parents of 2 and a half year old Liam, who was born with ARPKD and received peritoneal dialysis treatments at home for over a year before his death in July 2001.

As adults and parents, we all know, and try to teach our children, that heroes come in all shapes and sizes.

July 2000 was when the letter came - inviting the families of those who were living with various stages of renal failure (under the care of the Pediatric Nephrology team) to share their own stories – or simply, allow others to have a glimpse into their lives. Liam was a year and a half at that time – a few months home from surgery. Our lives were busy, to say the least. The theme of the project tugged on our heart strings, as we knew it was such a worthwhile undertaking, especially being a family who could directly understand the benefits of a book demonstrating that families and kids really can and do live with kidney disease – the operative word being "live", as opposed to the initial news we heard the day we were thrown into such a complex world of medical terms and diagnosis.

Little Heroes was the subject of this newly formed committee – a project that would move forward slowly and steadily lead by one of Liam's nurses who soon became a family friend. This project was close to the hearts of each and every one of her colleagues – the Nephrology team of Children's Hospital in Winnipeg – as well as to the families whose lives they had become a part of – a large "family" of sorts –

from a very different kind of world than we had been accustomed to.

As adults and parents, we all know, and try to teach our children, that heroes come in all shapes and sizes. From very early on in our lives, the myth and grandeur of heroic stories have been part of the teachings of our world – our lessons. In our preschool years, our parents, a favorite relative or fairytale character define our meaning and understanding of what a hero truly is – someone who makes us proud to either know them or try to live by their influence. As we become school children, there are teachers, authors and celebrities who enter our lives – expanding our world and our thoughts – heroes that become mentors. Growing into adulthood makes us more aware of everyday heroes. As young children, we saw this all along. What we realize, though, as adults, is that each and every one of us has the potential to become or act as a hero. We can instill belief in others, as they have in us. So, from husbands and wives, to the everyday person who stops to help someone who is lost, to the peacekeeper in a third world country not so far away – to the innocence and wonder of discovery within our children's minds – we discover heroes on a daily basis. Interestingly enough, it's only when heroes are recognized, only when someone publicizes (writes it, reports it, tells someone) do the heroes really get attention! History in itself creates heroes. Naturally, as we mature, our theories mature. So as we grow, our heroes grow to have more definition. Yet no matter how complex or how simple the message or credo which that individual delivers, we are awestruck just the same. Glen and I are privileged to realize that we know so many heroes – the mix of everyday people in our lives.

Our own Little Hero announced himself to the world on a chilly Wednesday afternoon, November 4, 1998 – the year of the Tiger. Already minutes old, he managed to make it through the amazing and complicated process of birth – how all Little Heroes have their beginnings. Heroes often change the course of others' lives – and Liam certainly did that – not only for us, but for our extended family, friends and the soon-to-be adopted family of supporters we would gain. A family that was familiar with the change of life patterns all-too-quickly. A family that was exposed to heroes most definitely on a daily basis. "It takes a village to raise a child" – a mantra my mom would often repeat, especially on the days we felt not quite as competent as we had thought parents should be. A part of this "village" was introduced to us two weeks prior to Liam's birth, after a routine ultrasound discovered that our son to be born had something called polycystic kidney disease – autosomal recessive, which statistics reported, would guarantee a short if non-existant life outside the safety of my womb.

Those of you who know of the disease know full well the challenges newborn and newly developed organs face against the complex, cystic kidneys within. The "family" we met helped us to understand that heroism outlives mortality. Heroes most often teach – Liam taught us more in his short lifetime than we could ever have expected to learn – about humanity, about dignity, about respect for this life we often take for granted. We read and asked all we could to understand this genetic condition. Our "Little Professor" left his world too quickly, but in a sense, endured for a long time within the challenged body that life dealt him.

It was during these two weeks before his birth that Glen and I chose a name for our son. We had no idea what a little fighter he was when we chose a name that meant "protection – a brilliant planner for the future who sets the pace for the race in life." By choosing this name, we somehow felt that by definition, we were arming him with protection from the impending battle looming ahead. And battle he did. Our minds shuffled quickly from thoughts of preparation for saying goodbye to saying hello to a world that seemed frightening – sleepless nights of worry as we spent endless hours learning to care for our firstborn child, gradually changing from "kid gloves" to the confident and caring hands of parents, as we maneuvered our way around a respirator and IV tubes in PICU, things that were required to help Liam gain strength for the day he would finally come home – breathing and taking the bottle on his own. Little victories that parents take for granted until shown how miraculous these acts truly are.

Liam's heroics were the result of touching many lives: to the medical professionals and people who entered his life specifically because of his condition, he allowed them to gain more insight and knowledge. He tested their diagnostic and surgical skills, their intensive, critical care and nursing skills, all the while himself learning to respond and thrive in part because of those skills – heroic to us and to him.

Through Liam's heroism we as parents were inspired, meeting his challenges head on, becoming not only his parents, but a part of his team. He taught us that we sometimes had to let go of the controls and have faith in each other – faith in the extreme and undying power of love. And because of his and our need for professional and time consuming care, we were inspiring others to perform everyday heroic deeds – the simple acts of providing meals and hospital visits – gifts of the heart from their own inspiration.

And what were we able to teach our "Little Professor"? He learned and understood at the beginning of his life that he also had to give up control, and quite literally put his life in our hands. He was accepted and loved unconditionally by all of us. He lived in a home filled with music and knew the joy of dancing in loving arms. His quiet, yet wholehearted laughter, many smiles and squeals of delight let us know that he thrived because of our goodness, our kindness and our compassion.

"It takes a village to raise a child" – a mantra my mom would often repeat, especially on the days we felt not quite as competent as we had thought parents should be.

Liam

So it was a few months prior to receiving the letter, that Liam underwent major and possible life threatening surgery, to remove one of the extremely enlarged cystic kidneys that were, by this time enormously taxing on the rest of his internal organs, making it almost impossible to digest food or breathe without assistance. This meant that if Liam survived his surgery, we would be moving into the extremely sterile world of dialysis – in his case, and for home use, peritoneal dialysis. Survive our boy did – with the strength of a tiger, he once again heroically pulled through hours of surgery and months of rehabilitation and change in lifestyle. But as heroes often inspire, ours certainly did – for we learned all about the process of dialysis at home and how to "connect" him as part of our bedtime routine – it was just another day in the life of living with kidney disease. Being home with our son was the most cherished time in our world.

Home care nurses, social and respite workers became a part of our daily lives – the ones who worked well with our family became our family, and our heroes.

Children's Hospital, though we adapted well over the months and years with long-term stays, was still not our peaceful home. We lived by the credo that "home is where your heart is" although most days, our hearts were split from each other, as Glen went to the office as much as he could, as well as took care of the house and our dog, Taz, while I stayed with Liam, hoping he would have the comforts of home no matter where we were, and that we would always be together. Daily, Glen, Liam and I reconnected with each other – trying to keep life as "normal" as we could. Everything that was available to us at the hospital was taken advantage of – from playrooms to music (live and recorded) to excercise and interaction with other playmates - adult hospitals could certainly learn a thing or two from the world of pediatrics!

Liam, in turn, inspired us to help others, by being a small part of the Children's Hospital fundraising awareness campaigns. So many other heroes inspired us as well, making it easier to speak of the challenges of our son's life, no matter how nervous and emotional life got at times. The medical world became less daunting the more we informed ourselves, with so many others to help us along the way. I'm sure to our friends it seemed like we were living in another country, although the more they came to visit us, the more they understood our "customs", and felt comfortable with the adaptations we had to make. As parents who are discovering what it's like to live with kidney disease – the ramifications, the rewards, the challenges – just trying to understand and absorb all of this information is what keeps you from crawling under a rock and staying there. Some days we really felt like we should have.

Yet in those dark times, somebody would always be around to see how we were – if there was anything that could be done to make Liam or us more comfortable or keep us more informed of his condition. More importantly, Liam himself kept us from "sinking". His reassuring smiles and eagerness for life was more inspiration than anything.

Home care nurses, social and respite workers became a part of our daily lives – the ones who worked well with our family became our family, and our heroes. Making marks on our lives, lending advice and organizational skills where we needed help (some days we really did) to remain as a family. Help with the medical issues, so we could concentrate on being a family – oh the peacefulness of it! Those who came around or worked at the hospital who shared stories about others or us, making us laugh and cry at different moments – stress relievers to help bring in the light of life. The other families and children that we met there humbled us every time we thought that no one else could understand what a bizarre, frightening, joyful life we lived. For to see what others had to deal with, in some strange way, allowed us not to feel so alone. Heroes everywhere, inspired by love for each other.

It's been three years since that letter arrived. In the time after his surgery and transition with home dialysis, we cherished the peaceful times more and more – the happy times of watching our son grow in his own way, continuing to discover life's simple pleasures that can only be captured as the wonder of a child does. We were glad that we could remain living in our "sanity space" – a ten acre spot just 40 minutes from Children's Hospital that allowed Liam to breathe fresh air, have the sun shine on his face, the snowflakes brush his eyelashes, the wind soothe his cheeks, and the green grass tickle his toes.

Liam

When Liam left us, I wanted so badly to continue his legacy by being a part of this project. Little did I realize that my grieving time would not allow this so quickly – how could I speak of the benefits of a life with kidney disease when Liam's outcome was what every family fears the most? But his presence remains strong, and because of that, we somehow are managing to survive without the physical presence of our son. Groups such as Compassionate Friends as well as the shoulders of those who knew our son well, help us to get through the difficult space without him – and the knowledge that it may take a lifetime to understand. Our minds and the minds of many around us have been exposed to a wealth of knowledge – not only in the realities of medical advances, but to the reason that these advances have truly worked – because of the integration of complementary care and conventional medicine. His death happened because it was time for him to move onto other teachings and to give his physical body a rest. Our son's life continued and thrived because of love and comfort and in knowing that he always had those simple things.

For those of you who have picked up a copy of this book – educate yourselves. But above all, don't consume yourselves. The benefits of life with your child far outweigh the difficulties simply because you are heroes to each other. One of the definitions of being a hero is to be the object of extreme admiration and devotion – as parents and families living with kidney disease, we are all proud and devoted to the well-being of our children. Every day, people are accomplishing heroic feats – that's what you are doing. By writing and telling our stories, we are learning from each other. The lives and unfortunate potential deaths of our children are not to be described as tragedies – that's what one of Liam's doctors reminded us in the days we tried to brace ourselves about his final days with us. There may be sadness, but there are no regrets. Writing, sharing and telling is important to our well-being. We thank our son daily for being our hero and our reason to continue living, and aspire to live with the strength that he had.

In closing, I'm reminded of the most important people Liam has inspired – little friends whose young minds are growing with the opportunity of having known him – who had no fear or hesitancy to understand Liam's challenged life. He was a part of their caring and love. In fact, two of these little friends have told us that they will continue to see Liam in their dreams – a place where he is free.

This story was shared with us by yet another one of our heroes – a woman who gives a tireless amount of energy to her own job, who deals with families on a daily basis that face more challenges raising their children than others do in this world. The story reminds us of what it's like to have your life changed by chronic illness, and still learn to live.

It's called Welcome to Holland --

I am often asked to describe the experience of raising a child with a disability to try to help people who have not shared that unique experience to understand it, to imagine how it would feel. It is like this: When you're going to have a baby, it's like planning a fabulous vacation trip – to Italy. You buy a bunch of guidebooks and make your wonderful plans. The Coliseum, the Michelangelo David, and the gondolas in Venice. You may learn some handy phrases in Italian. It's all very exciting.

After months of eager anticipation, the day finally arrives. You pack your bags and off you go. Several hours later, the plane lands. The stewardess comes in and says, "WELCOME TO HOLLAND!"

"HOLLAND??!!" you say. "What do you mean Holland?! I signed up for Italy! All my life I have dreamed of going to Italy!"

But there has been a change in flight plan. They have landed in Holland and there you must stay.

The important thing is that they haven't taken you to a horrible, disgusting, filthy place full of pestilence, famine and disease. It's just a different place.

So you must go out and buy new guidebooks. And you must learn a whole new language. And you will meet a whole new group of people that you would never have met otherwise.

It's just a different place. It's slower-paced than Italy, less flashy than Italy. But after you've been there for a while and you catch your

For those of you who have picked up a copy of this book – educate yourselves. But above all, don't consume yourselves.

🪰 *Liam*

breath, you look around and you begin to notice that Holland has windmills, Holland has Tulips, Holland even has Rembrandts.

But everyone you know is busy coming and going from Italy, and they're all bragging about what a wonderful time they had there. And for the rest of your life, you will say, "Yes, that's where I was supposed to go. That's what I had planned."

And the pain of that will never, ever, ever go away, because the loss of that dream was a very significant loss. But if you spend your life mourning the fact that you didn't get to go to Italy, you may never be free to enjoy the very special, the very lovely things about Holland!

Liam

Glossary

Alport's   A genetic disorder which causes hearing loss and kidney failure.

amniotic fluid   Fluid found around a fetus in a mother's womb.

ANCA   Anti-nuclear cytoplasmic antibodies; proteins found in the blood which may be associated with kidney disease.

ARPKD   Autosomal Recessive Polycystic Kidney Disease (see PKD).

biopsy   A procedure used to remove a piece of tissue from the body for examination under a microscope.

blood transfusion A procedure whereby a person receives blood donated by another person.

cadaver   The term used to describe a person who has died and is donating organs for transplant.

Calcitriol®   A medication used to help the body absorb calcium.

calcium   A mineral found in the bones and blood, important for bone growth and body function.

catheter/ catheterization   A small tube, usually made of a flexible plastic, placed into a patient's abdomen (peritoneal cavity) or a vein, allowing for the transport of dialysis fluid to and from the body.

cross match   A blood test done to check if a donor's blood type matches that of the recipient.

C-section (*cesarean section*)   A surgical procedure used to deliver a baby.

cyst   A fluid filled sac.

Cystinosis	A genetic disorder resulting in deposits of cystine (a protein building block) in the body organs, which can cause kidney failure.
diagnosis	A term used to describe a person's medical problem or condition.
dialysis	A procedure to remove excess water and waste from the body when the kidneys are no longer working.
dietitian	A professional who educates people about food and nutrition.
donor	A person who gives an organ (kidney or other) to another person for transplant.
Dysfibrogenemia	A clotting and bleeding disorder.
ECG	Electrocardiogram; a test to check the heart's function.
Ensure®	A high calorie liquid formula.
EPO®	Erythropoetin; a medication used with kidney disease that helps the body produce red blood cells.
ESRD	End-stage renal disease; also called *kidney failure* or *renal failure*. The point where the kidneys no longer function properly to remove excess water and waste from the body.
fetal assessment	A series of tests to monitor the growth and development of a baby in the womb.
gastrostomy tube	Also called a GT or a G-tube; a tube that is surgically placed through the skin into the stomach. It is used to feed a special formula through it, directly into the stomach.
growth hormone	A substance in the body which help children grow; in kidney failure, the growth hormone does not work properly, and children with kidney disease often receive injections of growth hormone to help them grow.

hemodialysis	"Hemo" – meaning blood; dialysis that uses a special machine and filter to clean the blood; it is usually done in the hospital 3 times per week for about 4 hours each time.
hernia	An abnormal buldge of tissue in certain parts of the body (ie. inguinal hernia – in the groin area), usually due to a rupture or weakness of the cavity that holds the tissue.
HUS	Hemolytic uremic syndrome; a syndrome which can lead to kidney failure.
immunosuppressed	The term used to describe a person who's immune system has been reduced through the use of special medications.
induced	The act of artificially starting the labour process of a pregnant woman.
kidney failure	Also called *renal failure* or *end-stage renal disease;* the point where kidneys no longer function properly to clean/remove water and waste from the body.
laparoscopy	A surgical operation used to insert a tube into the body and examine areas of the abdomen.
LRD	Living-related donor; the term used for a living person who is donating an organ (kidney or other) to another person for transplant.
match	The term used to describe an organ donor whose blood matches that of the recipient.
meds	Another term for medicines or medications.
neonate	A newborn baby.
Nephrologist	A doctor who specializes in looking after people with kidney disease.
N/G tube	Nasogastric Tube; a small plastic tube inserted into the nose, down the throat and into the stomach. It is used to feed people special formulas.
NICU	Neonatal Intensive Care Unit; a hospital ward specializing in the care of sick newborn babies.

OR	Operating Room; a special room where surgery is performed.
Pedialyte®	A specialized oral rehydration solution.
peritoneal dialysis	"PD" – a type of dialysis using a special plastic tube (catheter) that is surgically inserted into the abdominal cavity. Specialized dialysis fluid flows into the abdomen, contacting the peritoneal membrane. The membrane acts like a filter to clean the body's wastes and remove excess water.
PICU	Pediatric Intensive Care Unit; a hospital ward specializing in the care of sick children.
PKD/PCKD	Polycystic Kidney Disease; a genetic kidney disease causing large cysts to form in the kidneys which eventually cause kidney failure.
placenta previa	A complication of pregnancy when the placenta forms over the cervix opening instead of on the side of the uterus.
port-a-cath	A permanent catheter surgically placed under the skin which can be accessed with a needle to draw blood.
potassium	A mineral in the blood that is necessary to the body, but is harmful (can result in a heart attack) when it is not removed due to kidney failure.
Prednisone®	An immune suppressing medicine.
Prune Belly Syndrome	A syndrome children are born with which results in poor abdominal muscle development and kidney disease.
recipient	The person who receives an organ (kidney or other) from a donor.
reflux	Backward flow; used to describe the process of urine backing up into the kidneys from the ureters; may also describe the process of stomach contents backing up into the throat.

rejection	A process that involves a person's immune system attacking a transplanted organ because it thinks it is foreign to the body.
renal failure	Also called *kidney failure* or *end-stage renal disease;* the point where the kidneys no longer function properly to clean waste and remove excess water from the body.
respirator	A machine that breathes for someone who cannot breathe on their own.
restless leg syndrome	A syndrome thought to be related to an accumulation of waste products in the body resulting in a person moving their legs constantly.
rickets	A condition that causes softening and bending of the bones due to vitamin D deficiency; in kidney disease the body cannot activate vitamin D properly and if not treated, can result in bone deformity.
scans	A test that looks at the structure and/or function of the kidney (ie ultrasound).
Schimke Immuno-osseous Dysplasia	A genetic disorder affecting the white blood cells, bones and kidneys, which causes low white cells, short growth stature and kidney failure.
transplant	The process of taking a healthy organ (ie. kidney) from one person (donor) and surgically implanting it into another (recipient) person.
transplant list	The list that is kept of all people requiring a kidney transplant.
tube feed	The process of feeding a person through a tube with liquid nutrition/formula.
Urologist	A doctor who specializes in doing surgery for people with kidney and bladder problems.
ultrasound	A special test using sound waves to look at the size and structure of organs inside the body.
William's Syndrome	A genetic disorder causing developmental delay, high calcium blood levels, heart problems and occasionally kidney failure.

Little Heroes Project Team
Where would we be without our volunteers?

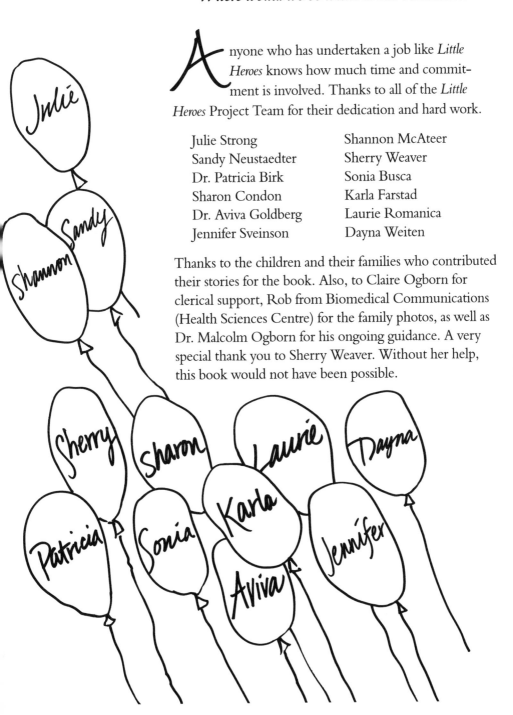

Anyone who has undertaken a job like *Little Heroes* knows how much time and commitment is involved. Thanks to all of the *Little Heroes* Project Team for their dedication and hard work.

Julie Strong
Sandy Neustaedter
Dr. Patricia Birk
Sharon Condon
Dr. Aviva Goldberg
Jennifer Sveinson

Shannon McAteer
Sherry Weaver
Sonia Busca
Karla Farstad
Laurie Romanica
Dayna Weiten

Thanks to the children and their families who contributed their stories for the book. Also, to Claire Ogborn for clerical support, Rob from Biomedical Communications (Health Sciences Centre) for the family photos, as well as Dr. Malcolm Ogborn for his ongoing guidance. A very special thank you to Sherry Weaver. Without her help, this book would not have been possible.

We would love to hear from you!

The Little Heroes Project team is interested in your thoughts about this book. Please let us know your comments by taking a moment to write them down and sending them to us.

_____

_____

_____

_____

_____

_____

_____

_____

You may mail your comments to:

The Little Heroes Project Team
c/o Pediatric Nephrology
FE009-840 Sherbrook Street
Winnipeg Manitoba
R3A 1S1

Or fax us at (204) 787-1075

ORDER FORM

If you would like to order more copies of Little Heroes – How We Live with Kidney Disease, please use the form below.

I would like to order: _____ copies at $10.00 each.

Please add $3.50 per book for shipping and handling.

Total enclosed is $_____

Please make cheque or money order payable to "Little Heroes Trust Fund" and mail along with order form to:

Little Heroes Trust Fund
c/o Pediatric Nephrology
FE009-840 Sherbrook Street
Winnipeg Manitoba
R3A 1S1

Name: _____

Address: _____

_____

Province: _____

Country: _____

Postal Code: _____

Telephone Number: (   ) _____